Design guide for applications of sandstone quarry sand in South Wales

M J Lamb

Viridis Report VR8

First Published 2005
ISSN 1478–0143
ISBN 1-84608-757-0

Acknowledgements

This document has been prepared by TRL Limited as the final deliverable of a two-year project to examine market applications for sandstone quarry sand in South Wales. Financial support has been provided by the RMC Community Fund under the Landfill Tax Credit Scheme and by the Welsh Assembly Government's Aggregates Levy Sustainability Fund, via the Environmental Body Viridis.

The assistance of Gerald Davies Landscaping Limited is acknowledged in the preparation of test slabs for pendulum and scuff testing during the field trials. They have also provided a site for the block paving trial and provided plant and labour to construct the cycle path.

The provision of specialist technical assistance by Richards, Moorehead and Laing on issues regarding the manufactured soils trials is gratefully acknowledged.

The Geoenvironmental Research Park project, led by Cardiff University's Geoenvironmental Research Centre contributed by procuring Minton, Treharne and Davies for the laboratory testing associated with the cycle path trials.

Jacobs Babtie provided Mr Rob Penman from their Bedford office to attend the steering group meetings and provide technical advice.

A steering group with cross industry representation was assembled, comprising the following members, and the input of these members to the project is also acknowledged:

Name	Organisation
Dr Murray Reid	Viridis
Dr John Lewis	TRL Limited
Mr Martin Lamb	TRL Limited
Mr Martyn Jones	TRL Limited (from January 2003 to January 2004)
Mr John Howells	RMC Aggregates South Wales (from January 2003 to January 2004)
Mr Paul Thompson	RMC Aggregates South Wales (replaced J Howells in January 2004)
Mr Mike Samuel	Hanson Aggregates
Mr Ivor Richards	Richards, Moorehead & Laing
Mr David Richards	Richards, Moorehead & Laing
Mr Sean Connick	Welsh Development Agency
Mr Geoff Marquis	Neath Port Talbot County Borough Council
Dr Geoff Baxter	University of Cardiff (from July 2003 to July 2004)
Dr. Talib Mahdi	University of Cardiff (replaced G Baxter in July 2004)
Mr Mike Hoult	Minton, Treharne and Davies
Mr Rob Penman	Jacobs Babtie Group

CONTENTS

Executive Summary

This document is a Design Guide for the use of sandstone quarry sand (SQS) in South Wales. It is aimed at clients, contractors and specifiers who may wish to use the material and planners who have to assess applications involving the use of the material.

Sandstone quarry sand is produced by the crushing and screening of the Pennant Sandstone at five quarries in South Wales. The crushed rock is valuable as an aggregate with excellent skid resistance properties, for use in the surface course of roads. Production of this aggregate however often leads to the generation of large amounts of fine material, known as sandstone quarry sand. The material is also referred to locally as sandstone dust and gritstone dust.

The material is very well graded from a maximum grain size slightly larger than 3.5 mm to a clay fraction, with around 15-20% of the material smaller than 75 µm, know as 'filler' or 'fines'. It is very consistent in grading and other properties. Exact levels of production are difficult to estimate, but it is likely that somewhere in the order of 0.9 million tonnes of SQS are produced in South Wales annually.

The material is a charcoal grey colour and its well graded nature allows for good particle interlock and correspondingly good compaction. The potential for the fines to absorb water however is a significant issue with the material, as whilst the material exhibits excellent strength at optimum moisture content (OMC), the strength decreases dramatically when wet of optimum. However, it can be mixed with cement to form a versatile material for earthworks applications, or with compost to form a manufactured topsoil.

This document aims to provide the reader with technical information on the material, to highlight applications that have been or are currently in use, and to disseminate the new applications that have been trialled as part of this study. A summary of the main applications is given in the following table. The aim is to encourage greater use of this valuable and versatile material.

Advantages of using sandstone quarry sand

Use of this material can reduce the demand for land won or marine dredged sand and gravel, thus preserving valuable natural resources. It also ensures that the material is being used constructively, rather than accumulating in stockpiles in quarries or being used for low-value applications. Use of the material, where appropriate, will therefore contribute to sustainable development and should be encouraged.

This Design Guide describes applications for which the material is suitable in South Wales. However, similar sandstone in other parts of the UK and elsewhere are also quarried for high skid resistance aggregates, resulting in the production of similar sandstone quarry sand. Many of the applications described may also be suitable in these other areas.

Summary of applications

Application / Advantages of SQS use	Potential difficulties with SQS use	Notes
Block paving bedding sand Cheaper than standard building sand. Environmentally more acceptable than marine dredged material. Compacts well at optimum moisture content.	Moisture very important – difficult to compact due to air voids if too dry. When wet it moves with the vibrating plate and does not compact well.	Guidance will need to be given to operatives if used.
Cycle paths Several of the quarries are located near to cycle routes – cost effective in such situations. Good compaction gives a firm surface. Surface finish smoother than many alternatives.	Moisture content is critical as is difficult to compact either side of optimum. Can crack during compaction if cement added when dry.	Guidance will need to be given to operatives if used.
Concrete Acceptable C30 grade concrete can be made using 12% SQS.	Filler increases water demand and hence increased cement is required.	If filler was removed a greater proportion of material could be used.
Block manufacture Cost effective compared to building sand. 7N/mm2 block can be manufactured using SQS.	Requires 10% 6mm grit to prevent balling and air voids.	–
Bentonite enhanced sand Mixes well with bentonite and cost effective. Large volume application. Established and accepted technology.	Inconsistent demand. Competes with local materials. Move away from landfill.	Potential for filler to be used if it could be stored on site.
Earthworks Well graded nature of unseparated SQS gives good compaction at optimum moisture content. Separated >75µm sand good drainage material	Moisture content and control is very important to ensure strength and ease of handling.	–
CBM1 sub-base Material mixes well with cement. 4% cement meets strength requirements. Cost effective if highway scheme near quarry.	Transport an issue. Competes with other materials that can be used in an unbound state.	Control of moisture content essential.
Cement extender May have some potential as a cement extender. Filler could be used, allowing >75µm material to be used for other applications	Logistical issues at quarry. Possibly not cost effective at present.	Potential to offset costs if >75µm fraction was sold for higher value applications.
Manufactured topsoil Allows unseparated SQS or filler to be used. Market for manufactured soil likely to increase. Production of compost from green waste likely to increase due to EC Landfill Directive. Consistent material. Forms good soil when mixed with green waste compost.	Fertiliser may be required for the material to meet the nutrient requirements of BS. Distance between quarry and compost processing facility critical to economics. Material manufactured from CD&EW fines looks more like a natural soil.	A range of mixes could be produced for specific applications.

2

Part 1: Issues

Plate 1 Stockpile of SQS in South Wales quarry

1 Introduction

This document is structured as follows:

- Section 1 gives an introduction to the issues regarding the material.

- Section 2 gives details on general material properties and properties of the quarry sand specifically.

- Section 3 concentrates on the applications considered

- Section 4 is a summary.

- Appendix A details the applications initially considered.

- Appendix B is a selection of case studies, which highlight existing or potential future uses of the material.

The Consultation Draft Minerals Technical Advice Note (Wales) – Aggregates (1) identified that approximately 3.8 million tonnes of crushed rock 'fines' are produced annually in South Wales, a significant proportion of which is from sandstone quarries.

The amounts of this material are increasing because modern methods of road surfacing use a higher proportion of the coarse aggregate from these quarries. There are markets for some of this material as a replacement for natural sand in construction, but this is insufficient to utilise all the material and large amounts are accumulating in sandstone quarries in South Wales. There is thus a need to develop innovative applications to utilise this material.

Following the crushing and screening processes, the sandstone quarries produce as much as 35% fines. The exact levels of annual production of sandstone fines are unknown, but Arup (2) have reported that somewhere in the order of 0.9 million tonnes of SQS were produced in South Wales 2001. This estimate was based on 35% of the sandstone production levels of 2.64 million tonnes reported by the South Wales Regional Aggregates Working Party (SWRAWP). The area covered by the SWRAWP covers 16 of the 22 Welsh counties, and approximately two thirds of the area of Wales including Powys and Ceredigion and all of the counties to the south. The production of sandstone is in the main confined to the area of the South Wales coalfield, stretching from Swansea in the west to Newport in the east and Merthyr Tydfil and the Brecon Beacons in the north.

The sandstone 'fines' consist of about 85% sand-sized material (above 75 μm) and 15% of silt and clay-sized material, known as 'filler'. In some quarries the filler is separated by washing and filtering processes, leaving clean sand that can be used in construction applications. This would however, leave approximately 15% or 135,000 tonnes of filler for which an application would need to be sought.

This design guide has been produced following a two year study of the material by TRL Limited. This included a literature review, a market research study undertaken by Richards, Moorehead and Laing, and a review of the physical and chemical properties of the material with additional analysis undertaken where there was a gap in the knowledge. Initially, over forty applications were considered, with the most promising applications in terms of size and value of market taken forward for further consideration. A table detailing the initial applications considered is presented in Appendix A. A series of laboratory and bench scale experiments were undertaken, with selected promising applications trialled at field scale.

The study investigated applications for the combined sand and filler, known as 'dust', and for the separate components. Priority was given to applications that use the untreated material, as this reduces the cost and ensures that no material is left which could end up unused.

1.1 Location of quarries

Sandstone is quarried at five locations in South Wales, shown in Figure 1 and is used predominantly as a high friction coarse aggregate for road surface courses. The Pennant Sandstone series in South Wales comprises sandstones of the Upper Coal Measures of Upper Carboniferous age (Namurian or Westphalian). The Pennant Sandstone is particularly prized as it has a high polished stone value (PSV); this is a measure of the resistance of a roadstone to the polishing action of a vehicle tyre. High friction road surface courses, made from aggregates with high PSVs, are essential as the state of surface polish is one of the main factors that will affect the resistance of the surface to skidding.

1.2 Who should read this document

Guidance is provided for clients, specifiers and contractors who may consider using Sandstone Quarry Sand (SQS) for the range of applications detailed in the document and for planning authorities who may be faced with applications to use the material. It should be of interest to government, regulatory authorities, infrastructure owners and operators, contractors, designers and the research community.

Relevant stakeholder groups include:

- National Government (i.e. Welsh Assembly Government).

- Local authorities.

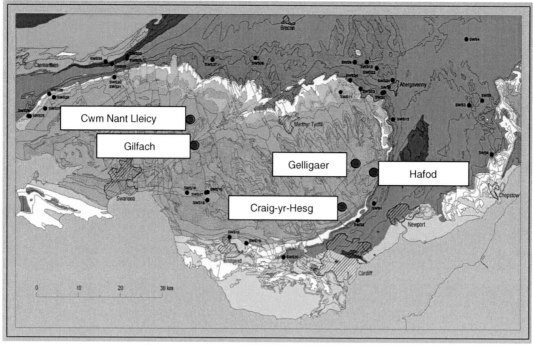

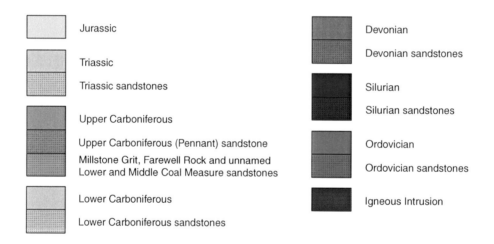

Jurassic	Devonian
Triassic	Devonian sandstones
Triassic sandstones	
	Silurian
Upper Carboniferous	Silurian sandstones
Upper Carboniferous (Pennant) sandstone	
Millstone Grit, Farewell Rock and unnamed Lower and Middle Coal Measure sandstones	Ordovician
	Ordovician sandstones
Lower Carboniferous	
Lower Carboniferous sandstones	Igneous Intrusion

Figure 1 Geological map of South Wales showing approximate location of sandstone quarries

- Regulatory authorities.

- Quarry owners and operators.

- Designers and consultants.

- Contractors.

- Research organisations and universities.

- Development agencies (e.g. the Welsh Development Agency).

- Infrastructure owners and operators (e.g. the Forestry Commission, country parks, local authorities, British Waterways).

- Planning authorities.

Part 2: Material properties

Plate 2 SQS compacted and uncompacted during cycle path trial

2 General material properties

As shown in Figure 1, Pennant Sandstone is of Upper Carboniferous age and is widespread across South Wales, often overlying the South Wales coal seams. It comprises predominantly sandstone greywacke made up of quartz, metaquartzite / quartzite and chert grains with a matrix comprising fine grained mica, microcrystalline quartz, amorphous iron oxides and opaque phases.

Plate 3 shows an outcrop of Pennant Sandstone in South Wales.

Plate 3 Outcrop of Pennant Sandstone

2.1 Physical characteristics

The 'dust' is well graded and varies from very fine clay (<0.002 mm) to fine gravel (2.00 to 6.00 mm), and is typically charcoal grey as shown in Plate 4 and Plate 5.

The filler fraction is generally a lighter grey in colour and ranges in size from 0 to 75 μm, and this material is shown in Plate 6 and Plate 7. When left to dry, the filler tends to form a crust on the surface whilst when wet the material will ball together, with a sticky consistency.

Three sets of physical test data from Gilfach quarry (2000, 2001 and 2002) have been made available to TRL, and are tabulated in Table 1. Physical testing is typically carried out on the 14 mm to 10 mm fraction in accordance with appropriate British Standards, and hence should only be used for indicative purposes only. The results give a general indication of the strength, shape and abrasiveness of the stone.

An aggregate with crushing and impact values of 25 or less would generally be considered suitable for use in asphalt. The values of 12 to 17 reported compare very favourably to the guideline values. The Los Angeles resistance to fragmentation values also reflect a strong aggregate.

Polished stone value (PSV) tests carried out on the aggregates give values in the range 70 to 72. The higher

Plate 4 Stockpile of SQS

Plate 5 Close up of SQS

Plate 6 Stockpile of filler

the PSV figure the greater resistance the aggregate has to polishing and an aggregate with a PSV over 60 is regarded as a High Skid Resistant Aggregate.

The physical analysis provided to TRL by RMC and Hanson, presented above, relates primarily to the use of the material as a roadstone. Whilst around half of the SQS produced is incorporated into asphalt mixes, the applications considered for this study are not part of the

Plate 7 Close up of filler stockpile

pavement wearing course. For this reason a number of more general engineering tests were undertaken by Minton, Treharne and Davies (MTD) laboratory in Cardiff and Babtie testing laboratory in Kent, and are presented in the following sections.

2.2 Quarry grading analysis

RMC and Hanson have supplied data to TRL from three quarries (Gilfach, Gelligaer and Craig yr Hesg).

The gradings from all three quarries are very similar and extremely consistent. Figure 2 represents the results of tests from Gilfach, showing the coarsest and finest gradings obtained from 30 sets of data, along with the mean and standard deviation gradings.

From the results of these tests, the sandstone quarry sand can be classified as a consistent, well graded silty sand. The consistency of the material can be seen in both Figure 2 and in the small ranges of fractions detailed as follows:

- Content of clay and silt fraction (<0.063 mm) ranges from 23% to 11%, averaging 14.6%.

- Fine sand (0.063 mm-0.200 mm) range approx. from 23% to 13%, averaging 17.3%.

- Medium sand (0.200 mm-0.600 mm) range approx. from 21% to 14%, averaging 18.2%.

- Coarse sand (0.600 mm-2.000 mm) range approx. from 37% to 23%, averaging 28.3%.

- Fine gravel (2.000 mm-6.000 mm) range approx. from 32% to 16%, averaging 21.6%.

- There are no medium gravel (6.000 mm-20 mm), coarse gravel (20 mm-60 mm) or cobble sized fractions (>60 mm) in the samples analysed.

Box 1 Grading analysis

Grading analysis, or particle size distribution is a measure of the particle / grain sizes of a given sample, based on the percentage of sample retained on, and passing through a series of sieves of progressively smaller mesh size to a minimum of 0.063 mm diameter.

Many engineering specifications will give a grading range or 'envelope' for an application which must be attained for a material to be used.

In many engineering applications, there is a limit on the percentage of fines (<0.063 mm diameter) permitted due to concerns over frost heave potential and difficulties in handling when wet.

Table 1 Physical properties of South Wales sandstone aggregate

Test	Year		
	2000	2001	2002
Particle density saturated surface dry (mg/m3)	2.64	2.64	2.61
Particle density oven dry (mg/m3)	2.60	2.60	2.58
Particle density apparent (mg/m3)	2.70	2.71	2.67
Water absorption (%)	1.4	1.4	1.3
Aggregate impact value oven dry	15	15	17
Aggregate impact value soaked	20 (10 blows)	18 (10 blows)	24 (9 blows)
Aggregate crushing value	14	14	14
Aggregate abrasion value	8	7.9	10.1
Ten percent fines value oven dry	270 kN	320 kN	260 kN
Ten percent fines value soaked	180 kN	230 kN	180 kN
Flakiness index	17	12	14
Elongation index	20	20	19
Resistance to fragmentation (LA method (%))	19	25	29
Resistance to wear (micro-Deval)	38	37	40

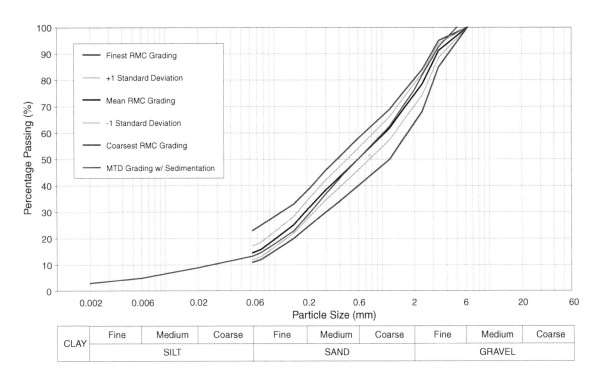

Figure 2 Particle size distribution results for Gilfach Quarry

Because of the high fines content a further particle size distribution test including a pipette sedimentation test was undertaken by MTD on another sample of the Gilfach material. Both tests were undertaken to BS 1377: Part 2:1990 (4) and allowed further analysis of the fine fraction. The results of this analysis, shown in Figure 2, indicate that of the average 14.6% passing the 0.063 mm sieve roughly 20%, approximately 3% of the total soil mass, are smaller than 0.002 mm and can be regarded as clays, the other 80% categorised as silts. This quantity of fines, both silts and clays is relatively high for a granular soil and will reduce the permeability of the soil, increase moisture retention and enhance the soil's susceptibility to frost heave.

The similarity between the contents of fine, medium and coarse sand, along with fine gravel and the proportion of fines, clearly shows the well graded nature of the material with no single fraction being considerably more prevalent than any other. However, an analysis of the materials D_{10} and D_{60} values, where D_{10} is the largest size of the smallest 10% of the material and D_{60} is the largest size of the smallest 60% of the material, will provide a figure for the coefficient of uniformity which will quantitatively describe the degree to which the material is well graded.

The D_{10} value of the Gilfach material is less than 0.063 mm in all cases and using the results from the later sedimentation test is seen to be approximately 0.025 mm. The D_{60} value ranges from 0.68 mm to 1.80 mm with a mean D_{60} value of 1.05 mm. Using the mean D_{60} value and the D_{10} value taken from the sedimentation tests it is possible to approximate the coefficient of uniformity (CoU) for the soil (D_{60}/D_{10}).

$$\mathrm{CoU} = \frac{D_{60}}{D_{10}} = \frac{1.05}{0.025} = 42$$

Box 2 Uniformity

The coefficient of uniformity is used to give a quantitative assessment of how well graded a material is. A value greater than 10 indicates a well graded soil. Smith (3) defines three categories:

- *Well graded* – the particle size distribution extending evenly over a wide range of particle sizes, without excess or deficiency in any particle size.

- *Uniformly graded* – having a particle size distribution over a limited range, i.e. all of the particles are generally the same size.

- *Poorly graded* – having a particle size distribution containing an excess of some particles and a deficiency in others.

From this approximation it is clear that the soil is a very well graded material. The well graded nature of the material, along with the relatively small particle sizes and relatively high fines content, suggest that the material will have a low permeability whilst during compaction it will achieve good densification due to close particle packing. The high silt content will encourage moisture retention but will make the soil more susceptible to frost heave. The particle shape is angular or sub-angular which, in association with close particle packing, will provide relatively high shear strength with a high angle of internal friction.

2.3 Plasticity

The plasticity of the fine (<0.425 mm) fraction of the sandstone quarry sand was expressed by means of the liquid and plastic limit tests (3). Table 2 summarises the analysis carried out on the material supplied from the three quarries.

The data are consistent for all three materials tested and show that the fines have low plasticity. The material cannot therefore be classed as a non-plastic granular material. The mean data taken together with the mean grading presented in Table 2, result in the material being classified in accordance with BS 5930 soil classification system (5) as a well graded clayey sand.

> **Box 3 Plasticity index**
>
> The plasticity index is the range of moisture contents in which a soil is plastic, and is calculated by subtracting the moisture content at the soils liquid limit by the moisture content at the soils plastic limit.
>
> *Liquid limit* – the moisture content at which a soil stops acting as a liquid and starts acting as a plastic solid.
>
> *Plastic limit* – the moisture content at which a soil stops acting as a plastic and starts acting as a brittle solid.

In terms of use as a Type 1 crushed rock, Clause 803 of the Specification for Highway Works (SHW) (6) requires that material passing the 425-micron BS sieve is non-plastic (see later discussion on frost heave). For this reason, the use of SQS in such an application would not be permitted. Additionally, Clause 804 (sub-clause 2) of the SHW, which covers Type 2 sub-base, permits material with a plasticity index of less than 6, indicating that SQS would not be suitable for this application either. Class 6F granular fills for use in capping applications (SHW Series 600) do not have plasticity limitations associated with them, and can make use of a wide variety of granular soil types. Accordingly, low plasticity SQS could be utilised in such an application, although the addition of a coarse fraction would be required. SQS does not meet the grading requirements for either fine (6F1) or coarse (6F2) capping. However, it could be brought into the 6F1 grading envelope by the addition of a coarse fraction.

Unpaved roads traditionally used an as-dug coarse gravel with a sand to clay sized matrix to bind the material together and to provide a degree of waterproofing. As such, SQS could readily find a use as a fine component in such an application.

2.4 Compaction

The behaviour of the material under compaction is critical for earthworks applications. Laboratory compaction testing in accordance with BS1377: Part 4: Method 3.7 (vibrating hammer) (7) was undertaken by MTD in August 2003 and the resulting compaction plots are reproduced in Figure 3. The results are summarised in Table 3.

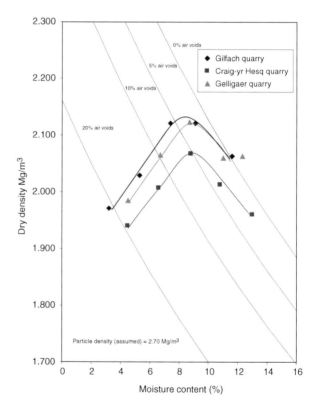

Figure 3 Compaction plot

Table 2 Plasticity index testing

Property	Gilfach (filler)			Craig yr Hesg			Gelligaer			Average
Percentage retained on 425 micron sieve (%)	0	0	0	60	68	68	66	67	70	66.5
Liquid limit (%)	29	30	29	24	25	25	23	24	25	24
Plastic limit (%)	19	20	19	17	18	17	18	17	17	17
Plasticity index	10	10	10	7	7	8	5	7	8	7

Table 3 Laboratory compaction testing

Property	Gilfach	Craig yr Hesg	Gelligaer	Mean
Maximum dry density (Mg/m3)	2.14	2.07	2.13	2.11
Optimum moisture content (%)	8.3	8.8	8.8	8.6
Air void content at OMC (%)*	3.1	5.1	2.5	3.6
95% relative compaction (Mg/m3)	2.03	1.97	2.03	2.01
Lower moisture content for 95% relative compaction (%)	5.0	5.3	5.8	5.4
Upper moisture content for 95% relative compaction (%)	12.3	12.6	12.3	12.4

Box 4 Compaction

When a material is compacted, the particles are pressed together to increase its density. This removes air and results in an increase in dry density. There are two main factors to consider when compacting a material; the physical properties (grading and particle shape) and the moisture content.

The grading and particle shape of a material will affect the degree to which it can be compacted – well graded materials compact well as the range of particle sizes serve to fill air voids and achieve high density. Rounded particles are more easily compacted as there is little mechanical interference.

The moisture content of a material will also have a significant effect on how well it can be compacted. Different water contents will produce different dry densities. The moisture content corresponding to the maximum dry density on plot (see Figure 3) is referred to as the Optimum Moisture Content (OMC).

The laboratory compaction plots presented in Figure 3 are very similar for the three samples tested. The maximum density falls between that to be expected for crushed rock Type 1 (typically 2.20 to 2.40 Mg/m^3, depending on source) and a well graded granular soil (typically around 2.00Mg/m^3). The mean optimum moisture content is relatively high (compared to Type 1) and reflects the concentration of fine, moisture retaining material in the grading. The moisture sensitive behaviour is also indicated by the relatively wide range of moisture content that results in 95% relative compaction (typically a 7% moisture content range). The well defined peaks of the compaction curves show that the SQS responds well to vibratory compaction, and supports the assumption of particle shape consistently being angular or sub-angular. Information from Hanson suggests that the natural 'stockpile' moisture content of the SQS dust is approximately 9%, slightly wet of optimum (see Section 2.6).

Ensuring that the moisture content of the material is at or close to optimum is critical for a number of applications, and practical experience of this will be discussed in greater detail later in this guide.

2.5 Strength

An assessment of the strength of the material as California Bearing Ratio (CBR) was undertaken in accordance with BS1377: Part 4 (7) and the results are presented in Table 4 and Figure 4. CBR is a measure of a material's resistance to penetration, expressed as a percentage of the value for crushed rock, and is widely used for pavement design in roads.

Table 4 Strength (CBR) testing

Gilfach		Craig yr Hesg		Gelligaer	
Moisture content (%)	CBR (%)	Moisture content (%)	CBR (%)	Moisture content (%)	CBR (%)
3.2	45	4.5	80	4.5	61
5.3	87	6.6	55	6.7	47
7.4	47	8.8	26	8.7	33
9.1	17	10.8	5.2	11.0	4.2
11.6	1.8	13.0	1.5	12.3	1.3

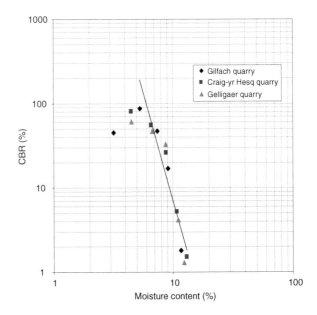

Figure 4 Strength (CBR) analysis

The mean optimum moisture content of 8.6% equates to a laboratory CBR of around 30%. This strength is higher than required for capping applications (15% laboratory CBR) and similar to the lower limit recommended for sub-base (at least 30% laboratory CBR). As such, the strength data indicates that SQS can contribute good load bearing characteristics when at approximately optimum moisture content. However, the susceptibility of the SQS to increased moisture content is clearly shown in Figure 4. The sharp drop off in strength with minimal added moisture beyond optimum, observed for all three samples, shows the susceptibility of the soils to additional moisture. A decrease in the CBR to 8% at 10% moisture content and less than 2% at a moisture content of 13% is a significant reduction from CBR 30% at 8.5% moisture content. This means that care must be taken in ensuring samples of SQS are close to, or below, the optimum moisture content when used in applications where strength is critical.

2.6 Moisture content

Hanson Aggregates have provided moisture content data for their Craig-yr-Hesg and Gelligaer quarries from January to April 2004. Samples were taken from both current production, and from the stockpile at each site, as presented in Table 5.

Table 5 Moisture content data

Moisture content %	Craig-yr-Hesg		Gelligaer	
	Production	Stockpile	Production	Stockpile
Number of samples	23	8	12	7
Minimum	1.4	6.3	1.5	5.5
Maximum	7.6	15.2	5.0	15.2
Average	3.0	9.7	2.7	9.7

Box 5 Moisture control

SQS compacts well to give a high quality fill material, but control of moisture is essential: if the material is too wet or dry it will not compact satisfactorily. Tests indicate that satisfactory compaction can be achieved over a range of moisture contents from about 5.5% to 12.5%.

Moisture is also critical for the strength of SQS with a sharp reduction in strength when wet of optimum: this is important if SQS is to be used for load bearing applications.

Table 5 shows that despite a relatively small sample size for the stockpiles, the range and average moisture contents from both quarries are quite consistent. The table also clearly indicates that SQS as produced has a much lower moisture content than from the stockpile, which would probably be expected, and that it falls well below optimum, whereas the average values in the stockpile are slightly above OMC. It might be the case that the moisture content of the stockpile during the summer months would be lower, but clearly care needs to be taken when both using and storing the material.

2.7 Frost heave

Fine grained materials, or well graded materials with significant fines content, such as SQS, have a greater potential to retain moisture than coarse grained materials if the fines are plastic. Frost heave is the result of the migration of moisture from deeper layers into the freezing zone in periods of freezing weather. As it freezes, vapour pressure is reduced and more water moves into the freezing zone due to capillary action. The potential for a material to be frost susceptible is critical when considering highway construction.

Frost susceptible material is deemed to be material with a mean heave greater than 15 mm, when tested in accordance with BS 812: Part 124 (8). In terms of SHW requirements, crushed rock is required to have less than 10% fines to avoid frost susceptibility and it is generally recommended that frost susceptible material shall not be used within 450 mm of a road surface. For applications with lighter loadings, such as cycle paths that do not experience vehicular loading, this requirement is less critical.

Frost heave testing in accordance with BS812 Part 124:1989 was carried out. A particle size distribution analysis was carried out for each of the materials using wet sieving, with the maximum dry density and moisture contents of both the quarry materials and a control stable trial specimen then recorded. The heave of both the reference sample and quarry sample was then tested over the period of 96 hours, as summarised in Table 6.

The results of the analyses clearly indicate that there is significantly greater heave from the materials from all of the quarries than from the reference samples, and the laboratory reported that all of the materials are frost susceptible, i.e. there was a mean heave of greater than 15 mm. Whilst this was not unexpected, it is considered that the values recorded will be of use as a reference for extrapolation if the material is, for example, mixed with coarser aggregate for use as an unbound sub-base.

2.8 Physical testing conclusion

The testing shows that the engineering characteristics and behaviour of the SQS from the three individual quarries are virtually inseparable, and is in part related to the original depositional environment of the sandstone

Table 6 Results of frost heave testing

Heave of sample after 96 hours	Specimen 1	Specimen 2	Specimen 3	Mean	Range
Craig-yr-Hesg	20.5 mm	23.5 mm	23.0 mm	22.3 mm	3.0 mm
Craig-yr-Hesg reference sample	11.0 mm	10.0 mm	11.5 mm	10.7 mm	1.5 mm
Gilfach	36.0 mm	33.0 mm	33.0 mm	34.0 mm	3.0 mm
Gilfach reference sample	14.0 mm	13.0 mm	12.0 mm	13.0 mm	2.0 mm
Gelligaer	30.5 mm	26.0 mm	26.0 mm	27.5 mm	4.5 mm
Gelligaer reference sample	14.0 mm	13.0 mm	12.0 mm	13.0 mm	2.0 mm

sequence and also the processing undertaken at the quarries. This feature of SQS can be viewed as a positive advantage in terms of developing general specifications for niche applications, as consideration of significant variability between local sources may be discounted. Whilst the results of most of the tests have been positive, showing good strength characteristics, a potential problem has been highlighted. Due to the relatively high fines content of the SQS, approximately 15% < 63μm, it has been seen that the material is very susceptible to an increased moisture content, with a significant reduction in load bearing capacity when wetted beyond optimum. The material is also susceptible to frost heave. For this reason, care must be taken in selecting suitable applications for the material and in ensuring the correct moisture content is used throughout any laboratory testing, field trials or full-scale applications.

2.9 Chemical analysis

Chemical analysis was provided for SQS from Gilfach quarry and 14 mm aggregate from both Gilfach and Craig-yr-Hesg quarries. It reveals that the material is comprised of around 78-80% silica (SiO_2), 10% Alumina (Al_2O_3),

4% Ferric Oxide (Fe_2O_3), 2.5%, Potash (K_2O) and 1% Magnesia (MgO) with various other trace elements making up the remainder of the material. The values are extremely consistent for both SQS and the 14 mm aggregate, and both materials have a loss on ignition of around 2 – 3%.

A further nine samples were analysed for specific applications as detailed in Table 7. Three samples were taken from each of three selected quarries to undergo testing, with the average values presented below.

The data from the above table indicates that the material is, once again, consistent, despite the fact that the sample from Gilfach was filler. The filler material is seen to have a higher electrical conductivity than the sand material from Craig yr Hesg and Gelligaer, due to the higher specific surface area of the fine grained fraction. The other main difference is that there is a noticeably smaller total solids content in the filler material, compared to the sand, possibly due to the fact that the filler is damped down during the extraction process at the asphalt plant. There is a corresponding higher loss on ignition and moisture loss in the filler from Gilfach compared to the

Table 7 Chemical testing

Determinand	Method	Unit	Gilfach filler*	Craig yr Hesg sand*	Gelligaer sand*
Electrical conductivity @ 20°C	AES 1035	μS/cm	221.67	127.00	94.67
Nitrogen as N	BS 3882:1994 modified	% wt	0.07	0.05	0.02
Phosphorous	MAFF method 59 modified	mg/kg	1.03	3.56	6.77
Potassium	MAFF method 63 modified	mg/kg	176.33	151.00	99.00
Acid soluble sulphate as SO_4	ICP	%	0.03	0.03	0.03
Water soluble sulphate as SO_4	ICP	g/l	0.02	0.05	0.03
Total sulphur as S	ICP	%	0.07	0.07	0.03
Total solids	AES 1023	%	85.09	97.86	96.41
Loss on ignition	950°C +/- 25°C	%	6.73	4.97	3.73
Moisture loss @ 105°C	105°C	%	0.67	0.43	0.47
Estimation of lignite content	**	%	4.93	3.40	1.20
Pyritic sulphur (FeS2)	BS1016 modified	%	0.09	0.11	0.05

* Average of three samples from each quarry.

** Lignite estimated by combustion and gravimetric recovery of CO_2, and assumed to comprise approximately 50% carbon and to be the only source of recovered CO_2. Combustion carried out at 650°C.

SQS from the other two quarries. The lignite content from the Gilfach filler is significantly higher than the other materials, which could potentially be explained by the smaller overall particle size. It is noticeable however, that the lignite content from the SQS from Craig-yr-Hesg quarry is also significantly higher than the samples from Gelligaer. The same is also true of the pyritic sulphur where the average concentrations recorded at Gelligaer are half those recorded at Gilfach or Craig-yr-Hesg. This could possibly be an issue if the material is used for concrete applications.

There is also noticeably less phosphorous in the filler material than the sand, although the values vary quite considerably throughout the three samples. In general there are very low concentrations of both nitrogen and total sulphur, with trace concentrations of phosphorous and potassium. The low level of nutrients is discussed for landscaping applications in Section 3.3.

Part 3: Applications

Plate 8 Trial of SQS as block paving bedding sand

3 Applications

This section covers the various applications either known to have been successfully used previously or examined as part of the research project. The applications will be considered in the context of South Wales, however, the general principles will be relevant to other geographical areas with similar materials.

There are a number of potential earthworks applications for the material which include general use as engineering fill. Alternatively, the material has been successfully used as a landfill liner material once mixed with bentonite. The material can also be mixed with Ordinary Portland Cement (OPC) for used as a cement bound road sub-base layer, or can be used alone, with OPC or with coarser material for use in footway or cycle path applications.

The material can be used in a variety of construction applications including incorporation into structural (C20 – C50) concrete mixes and concrete blocks. The material can also be used as a replacement building sand in certain applications and as a replacement laying course sand for block paving. There is also potential scope for the material to be used as a cement extender.

A successful application trialled was the use of the material in manufactured topsoil in conjunction with composted green waste. This application was also found to be suitable for the filler.

Should the material be separated, the course material would be suitable as a replacement for marine sand in a variety of applications including a high volume application of mixing with soil on playing fields to improve the drainage.

More detailed information on the applications discussed are presented in the following sections, and also in the case studies provided in Appendix B. A summary table of the applications is provided in the Executive Summary.

3.1 Earthworks

3.1.1 Bentonite enhanced sand in liner systems

Landfill sites, and certain contaminated land redevelopment sites generally require some form of low hydraulic conductivity physical containment system for base liner and/or capping construction. SQS can be used as part of a liner system if mixed with bentonite to form bentonite enhanced sand (BES).

Surface-constructed liner systems can comprise one or more layers of natural and/or synthetic materials. The applicability of the system will depend on the characteristics of the materials used to construct the system and their compatibility with the contaminants present.

The barrier materials used to construct liner and cover systems fall into a number of broad categories, i.e:

● Geomembranes.

● Low permeability compacted mineral materials:

 – Natural clay minerals.

 – Processed soil materials.

● Other barrier materials:

 – Geosynthetic clay liners (GCL).

 – Asphaltic concrete.

 – Soil-cement.

Although these barrier materials can be used as a single liner system, the often conflicting range of requirements for landfill liners (such as chemical / biological / damage / disturbance resistance) are best served by a composite liner system comprising two or more of these materials in contact with each other.

The low permeability compacted mineral materials are essentially cohesive soils. These cohesive soils may be natural, such as local clays; or processed, such as BES.

In addressing the requirements for landfill liners and the chemical effects on the materials available, due consideration should be given to the fact that strong acids and alkalis can dissolve solid material in processed soils, form solution channels and increase hydraulic conductivity. The effect on hydraulic conductivity is related to the concentration of the acid or alkali, the duration of the reaction, the temperature and the mineral composition. Processed mineral barriers, such as BES liners, contain only a relatively small percentage of clay minerals and are therefore particularly susceptible to chemical attack, since a small percentage loss of clay minerals can significantly affect the barrier performance. BES host materials should be non-reactive in the leachate environment, and limestone quarry sands are therefore not deemed to be suitable as host materials for BES. SQS is much less reactive chemically and hence better suited for this application.

BES needs to be designed for the sands available and for the performance required. A level of hydraulic conductivity of $1 \times 10\text{-}10$ m/s^{-1} or less, requires a bentonite content in the order of 6% and the grading of the host sand should all pass the 20 mm sieve, with no more than 10% passing the 0.063 mm sieve. The grading requirements quoted should be regarded as outline requirements that may need to be revised following the design process.

If it can be demonstrated that some other host material, e.g. SQS, can meet the performance requirements then there is no reason for it not to be used.

Local experiences

SQS has been used as BES for the construction of a number of new landfill cells in South Wales. The new landfill cells were successfully constructed using a composite liner system with a GCL primary barrier and a BES secondary barrier.

It should be noted that BES liners are generally in the order of 0.5m thick and that a 'typical' cell would be in the order of 25,000m^3. New landfill cells can therefore represent a significant demand for available resources of SQS.

3.1.2 Engineering fill

SQS is suitable for use in general fill, such as embankments. This would be a comparatively low value application, and as such there are likely to be a number of other materials that would potentially compete in such an instance such as processed construction, demolition and excavation waste (CD&EW). Given the likely low value of this application, the cost of transport would be a major factor in its viability, and the use of SQS as fill might be limited to occasional schemes in close proximity to a quarry. However, it may be particularly useful in situations where a material with consistent properties and appearance is required, possibly for aesthetic reasons. Natural fill materials can be highly variable, and the composition of CD&EW can vary significantly depending on the source of the material.

Concerns over moisture susceptibility and frost heave would prevent its use in unbound sub-base, without processing to remove or dilute the filler fraction. It is known that a quarry in the Republic of Ireland washes out the filler material to form an acceptable non-plastic sub-base, and it is understood that a number of trials have been undertaken using admixtures to stabilise or break down the clay minerals in the filler with limited success.

3.1.3 Cement bound material

Assuming that separation of the filler fraction was not considered appropriate for the material to be used as an unbound sub-base, the material could still be used as cement bound sub-base if economic.

Cement bound material (CBM) has five classes, with increasing 7-day strength requirements ranging from 4.5 MPa for CBM1 to 20 MPa for CBM5. The grading envelope for the materials to be included also becomes increasingly stringent from CBM1 to CBM5, with SQS only meeting the grading envelope for CBM1. CBM1 and CBM2 are restricted to use in the road sub-base, whereas CBM3, CBM4 and CBM5 are permitted to be used in the road base. Cement bound SQS has the potential to replace granular Type 1 sub-base.

Road design varies considerably depending on the trafficking requirements. Presented in Figure 5 is a typical cross section of a highway.

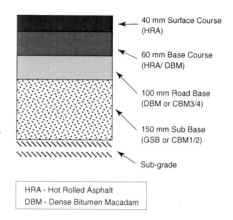

Figure 5 Typical road cross section

Testing was undertaken to determine the quantity of cement required to meet the 7-day strength requirements of CBM1 (4.5N/mm^2) in fully compacted samples. Tests were carried out in accordance with BS1924:Part2:1990 (9) and the results are shown in Figure 6. Mixes were carried out at 25, 50, 75, 100 and 125 kg/m^3 cement contents based on a density of 2,200 kg/m^3.

Test cubes were compacted at a moisture content of 9% by mass of aggregate, which is the OMC of the material. Three 150 mm cubes were made at each cement content, cured in accordance with BS1924 and crushed at seven days. The mean results of the testing are presented in Figure 6.

The graph above shows a steady increase in compressive strength with cement content, with the 4.5 N/mm^2 requirement for CBM1 as detailed in the Specification for Highway Works (6) falling between cement contents of 75 and 100 kg/m^3, at around 87.5 kg/m^3. In practice the higher cement content (100 kg/m^3) would be used to ensure the strength was achieved. This equates to around 4% of cement.

3.1.4 Cycle paths / footways

For unbound applications, or applications with lighter loadings such as cycle paths, the potential for frost heave would be less critical and the material could be readily used. For this reason, two experimental sections of cycle path were constructed at Afan Argoed Country Park in February 2004.

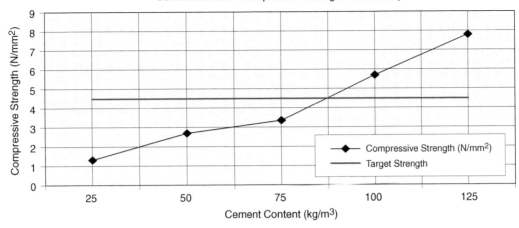

Cement Content / Compressive Strength Relationship

Figure 6 Graph of cement content vs. compressive strength

The trial comprised two separate test lengths which incorporated a range of designs and construction techniques. For the purposes of assessing the performance of SQS in cycle path applications it would be desirable to lay various test strips in a range of terrains and conditions to be able to observe their relative performance. However, for this initial trial only two scenarios were investigated. The main trial area was a 60m length of existing cycle path that was divided into 3 sub-sections. This was located on a reasonably straight and level section of existing cycle path that offered a uniform foundation and consistent protection from weathering along its length. The second trial area was on an exposed downhill left hand bend that is subject to surface water erosion and increased wear due to cyclists braking and turning, effectively a 'worst-case' scenario for wear. This area was approximately 11m in length.

The performance of the different trial sections and mix designs were assessed by visual inspection through regular monitoring.

Plate 9 View along the main trial section after construction

Plate 10 View of second trial area on exposed bend

Trial Area 1

Three construction combinations were investigated for area 1, namely:

- 20 metres compacted SQS.

- 20 metres SQS mixed with OPC, sub-divided into four 5 metre sections of 1%, 1.5% , 2% and 2.5%. OPC raked into the surface and compacted.

- SQS laid on 75 mm thick layer of 0 – 40 mm scalpings.

Trial Area 2

This area had an inside radius of 7m and an outside radius of 11m. For safety reasons, the material for this section was premixed on a flat area at the top of the slope. Twenty five buckets of SQS were mixed in with two and a half bags of OPC, giving approximately 4.2% OPC. This higher percentage was considered appropriate given the likely high wear the bend would be subjected to.

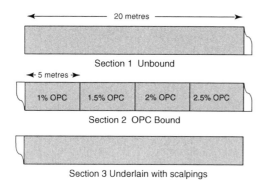

Figure 7 Trial Area 1 layout

Plate 11 Raking the OPC in to the SQS

Compaction

Compaction was achieved using 16 passes of a single drum roller, in accordance with the compaction requirements of Table 6/4 of the 600 series of the Specification for Highways Works. The passes were applied in 4 sets of 4. After the first three sets it was noticeable that the SQS was below optimum moisture content as it was not binding together very readily. Two gallons of water were sprinkled across the surface before the final set of passes was applied.

Samples of the as-delivered SQS taken for moisture content determination showed it to have a moisture content of 1.6% which was well below the 8.3% optimum value derived from earlier laboratory testing. This low moisture content is consistent with the 'as-produced' figures presented in Table 5, and indicates the importance of the moisture content in construction schemes.

SQS and OPC

After observing the difficulty in compacting the SQS in the first part of the trial length due to the low moisture content, the sand for this area was pre-wetted. This was achieved by adding water to the stockpile of sand and mixing it in with the mini-excavator. Samples of this material taken for subsequent moisture content determination showed it to have a moisture content of 4.7%.

The four sub-sections, one for each percentage of OPC, were constructed consecutively starting with the 1% OPC by mass. After tipping and levelling the SQS to the correct surcharged depth to provide a finished thickness of 50 mm, the OPC was spread over the surface, then mixed in to the SQS by raking over the surface as shown in Plate 11.

A Benford 171E single drum roller was used to compact this and all of the subsequent sections. This roller had a drum width of 0.7m and a mass of 476kg putting it into the 450-700kg per width category. Compaction was not undertaken until all four sub-sections had been constructed. As this roller was wider and heavier, compaction was achieved using 12 passes along three roller widths, and these were applied in three lots of four passes. It was observed that the sub-section containing 2.5% OPC showed signs of roller-induced cracking. It is likely that despite pre-wetting the SQS and adding water before rolling the moisture content might have been slightly dry of optimum and the quantity of OPC on this section might have been enough to draw sufficient moisture from the SQS to induce cracking during rolling.

Scalpings with SQS

After digging out the top 50-75 mm of existing cycleway with the mini-excavator, optical levels were taken on the finished loose surface and the wooden batons were placed along the edges of the section such that they were positioned on top of the original ground surface. The scalpings were placed to a nominal loose thickness of 75 mm and optical levels were repeated to give the actual thickness of uncompacted scalpings. The 20m length was then divided into two 10m sub-sections. The first 10m length had pre-wetted SQS applied to it and the second 10m length had as-delivered SQS spread over it which was then watered in as it was spread and raked. The intention of this technique was that the drier material would penetrate into the scalpings and the water would help wash it in. Plate 12 shows the SQS being spread over the scalpings and the colour difference indicates the difference in moisture content between the as-delivered and pre-wetted sand.

The Benford 171E single drum roller was used to compact this section as before. Finally, the edge restrains were removed and the edges rolled to provide the chamfered finish.

Plate 12 As-delivered SQS being spread after laying the pre-wetted material

Trial Area 2: SQS and OPC

Due to the location of this trial area, i.e. on a downhill bend, it was impractical to lay out the wooden edge restraints; instead the width was increased to provide an additional mass of material to the sides which would act as lateral restraint.

The existing surface was scarified using the mini-excavator and the loosened material was raked to provide a reasonably uniform surface. This was then lightly dusted with cement to help the SQS bind to it.

The material used for this trial area was the pre-wetted SQS mixed with approximately 4.2% OPC by mass. This mixed material was then tipped and spread over the trial area to a loose level of about 50 mm, as shown in Plate 12. After it had been raked level it was compacted using the Benford 171E single drum roller. Eight passes of the roller were applied along four roller widths. It was not possible to apply any further passes as the roller slipped on the surface due to the gradient of the section

Plate 13 Raking out the SQS and OPC on Trial Area 2

and the turning action of the roller due to the bend was causing the surface to crack. Once the material had been rolled, a brushed texture was applied to the surface using a stiff broom.

Construction thickness

For the main trial section only (Trial Area 1) optical levels were taken on the existing surface before applying the SQS and scalpings and again after compaction so that the compacted layer thicknesses for each sub-section could be determined. For the section with scalpings, the loose laid thickness was also recorded before the SQS was applied. Levelling positions were along the centreline of each section and lines 600 mm to either side from 0.5m to 19.5m along the section length at 1m intervals. Monitoring of the cycle path levels to assess any change was undertaken in early November 2004. As previously, points along the centreline and 600 mm either side were measured and at 1 m intervals. Whilst these points will not have been exactly the same as those measured in February, the 60 measurements per 20 m section should give a good indication of the overall performance of the track. The average thicknesses for each sub-section when laid, and the changes in level measured in November are shown in Table 8.

Table 8 Measured thickness of laid material

Material Sub-section	Compacted thickness (mm)		Average change in level since February*
SQS			
As found surface	46.1		-2.46 mm
Scarified surface	49.1		+4.05 mm
SQS + OPC			
1%	45.5		-2.94 mm
1.5%	42.7		-0.64 mm
2%	47.4		-0.52 mm
2.5%	51.0		+4.50 mm
Scalpings + SQS			
	Scalpings**	SQS+ Scalpings	
Pre-wetted	98.2	123.5	-4.03 mm
As delivered	71.3	106.1	+4.46 mm

* + = Upward movement - = Downward movement

** The thickness of the scalpings was the loose laid thickness.

Performance assessment

The assessment of the long-term performance of the trial areas was made from visual observations to see how well the different materials withstood weathering and their durability when subject to pedestrian and cyclist use, and the findings are presented below.

Unbound SQS

Surprisingly, of all the materials, the unbound section appeared to perform the best. After eight months of use the section appeared to have worn well and showed no signs of deterioration. Measurement of the levels suggests that the section that was scarified first has performed better that the as found surface as it has had an upward movement. In reality, this is more likely to be due to the small differences in the survey points in February and November, bearing in mind that the average overall increase in height is only 0.8 mm, and it is unlikely that the material has risen overall.

OPC bound SQS

The 2.5% OPC bound sub-section very quickly took on a concrete like appearance, although this appearance was observed some months later in the 2.0% and to a lesser degree 1.5% OPC bound sections. The 1% bound section had a similar appearance to the unbound material. The contrast between the 2.5% OPC section and the SQS laid on scalpings is shown in Plate 14. The OPC sections did not look as aesthetically pleasing as the unbound material, although in areas of higher use, and potentially urban areas there may be benefits in the addition of OPC.

Plate 14 2.5% OPC and scalpings interface

It was noticeable towards the end of the trial that the edges of the OPC sections appeared to have crumbled. It is assumed that this was caused either by water run-off from the track or water flowing against the edges of the track. Plate 15 shows the deterioration of the edges typical of the entire OPC bound section. Measurements of the change in levels show that 3 of the 4 sections appear to have had a downward movement with only 1 area having an upward movement, but on average there is an overall upward movement of 0.1 mm. The survey points were not near enough to the edges to record any reduction in levels as a result of this damage.

Plate 15 Edge deterioration on 2% OPC section

SQS with scalpings

The scalpings section initially held up very well, and was similar in appearance to the unbound layer. However, by late October 2004, a noticeable channel had appeared as shown in Plate 16. Discussions with the Ranger from Afan Argoed reveal that the damage was caused by a culvert overflowing on two occasions due to heavy rain. Clearly, a large volume of water would cause significant washout of any unbound material, and the damage cannot be attributed to any failing of either the material or construction method. Measurement of the levels again showed an average upward movement of 0.22 mm, probably due to the position of the survey points, although the survey points generally did not reach the main channelled area which may have indicated more of a downward movement trend.

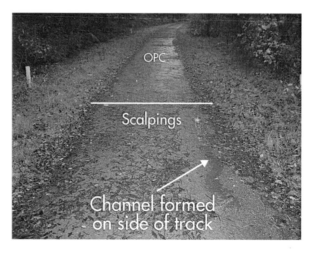

Plate 16 View of channel formed in scalpings section

It should be considered, however, that whilst there may have been some damage to the edge of the scalpings section and the edges of the OPC section, the main survey points in the central area of the path, i.e. the area that would receive the highest amount of pedestrian and cycle traffic, has effectively shown no deterioration.

Rangers from both NPT CBC and from the Forestry Commission have indicated that they are extremely pleased with the performance of the material and that they have used the small stockpile of SQS that was left over from the works for general repairs of the tracks and paths around the site.

Summary

The trials were extremely valuable as a learning experience in aiding the development of construction techniques. The control of moisture is critical for handling and compaction of the material, particularly on the 2.5% OPC bound section where roller induced cracks were caused through having too little moisture.

As a result of the success of the trial, a local BMX track was resurfaced using SQS, which is summarised below.

Plate 17 Compacting SQS used on BMX track

> **Box 6 Lessons learnt**
>
> Whilst the performance of the unbound material appears to be superior to that of the OPC bound SQS, if OPC bound material were to be used on a contract, an appropriate batch mixing plant would be required for extensive construction.
>
> Overall the SQS has performed very well and appears to have considerable potential as a surfacing material for cycle paths and footpaths, especially where a natural appearance is important.

3.1.5 Britton ferry BMX track

Following the successful cycle path trial described above, TRL were commissioned by Groundwork Neath Port Talbot and Neath Port Talbot Communities First Programme to design and supervise the resurfacing of a local BMX track. It was determined that the material would be used unbound, with 1.5% OPC on the ramps to provide additional stability. Construction was again undertaken by Gerald Davies Ltd using the same methods as above. One small difference was that the wooden boards were placed around the track to retain the material.

The material performed well, although as the material was very dry when delivered, water needed to be added to ensure adequate compaction. Plate 17 shows compaction being undertaken.

As the track has only recently been completed, there is no data available on long-term performance.

3.2 Construction

3.2.1 Block making aggregate

SQS is known to be used in block manufacture already. It is understood that the addition of 10% of 6 mm aggregate to the mix prevents balling and voids – two of the main reasons for the previous limited acceptance of the material. Whilst the 6 mm aggregate is relatively expensive, the additional costs are more than offset through the additional use of SQS.

It is understood that a number of block manufacturing companies in South Wales use SQS in their mixes at various rates, and that the blocks achieve the required 28-day strengths of 7 N/mm^2. A local block making company confirmed that strength testing on the most recent yield of blocks reported 7-day strengths of 9.3 N/mm^2.

3.2.2 Concrete

Hanson Aggregates manufacture structural concrete at a plant located within Craig-yr-Hesg quarry using 12% unseparated SQS. Crushed concrete cubes from the quarry have been supplied to TRL, which have 7-day strengths of 32.0 and 34.0 N/mm^2. It is understood that the product is being sold as standard C35 strength concrete. The strength requirements of C35 concrete (i.e. 35 N/mm^2) are based on 28 day measurements. As the strength of concrete increases over time, the 7-day strengths of 32 and 34 N/mm^2 recorded would be considerably higher than 35 N/mm^2 after 28 days.

If the material filler were to be removed at the quarry for other purposes, then a far greater proportion of the coarser grained material could be incorporated into the mix.

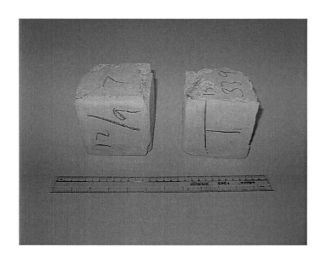

Plate 18 Concrete cubes supplied to TRL after testing

3.2.3 Building sand

It is understood that a number of quarry sands are sold as 'stone dust' as a sand replacement by various local builders merchants. Whilst the material is unlikely to meet building sand specifications, there is no reason why the material could not be used for small scale DIY projects, for example, concrete bases for patios etc, as long as it was understood that the sand to cement ratio would need to be reduced to account for the higher fines content.

3.2.4 Block paving bedding sand

Another potential use for SQS is as bedding sand for block paving and slabs. However, SQS is excluded from this use in the relevant British Standard (see Box 7). No clear reason is given for the reluctance to use crushed rock fines although it is believed to be due to the high moisture retention, and hence potential frost susceptibility of such materials. Another possibility is that the compaction of angular particles, such as SQS, require greater effort, and there is a potential risk of later settlement if the material is not compacted adequately. As discussed earlier, however, the well graded nature of SQS allows compaction to high density and low air voids.

The main requirement for laying course sand is to fit within the grading envelope set for each of the five types of use described above. Investigations using the PSD data obtained from RMC and Hanson shows that unseparated material fails to meet any of the grading envelopes, even for type IV. However, when split at the 75 µm sieve size the coarse fraction, 75 µm to 3.5 mm, comfortably meets the grading requirements for type IV and type III and just meets the requirements for types IA, IB and II.

It is understood however, that the requirements for laying course sand are occasionally overlooked and SQS has already been used successfully by contractors in South

Box 7 Specification

British Standard BS 7533: Part 3 1997 (10) provides the specification for block paving laying course sand. The standard classifies the potential applications of paving into five classifications.

- IA – Pavements receiving severely chanalised trafficking, aircraft pavements and bus stations.

- IB – Industrial pavements and loading bays.

- II – Adopted highways and other roads, petrol station forecourts, pedestrianisation projects with regular heavy trafficking, car parks receiving some heavy trafficking and footways regularly overridden by vehicular traffic.

- III – Pedestrianisation projects receiving only occasional heavy traffic and car parks receiving no heavy vehicles.

- IV – Private drives, areas receiving pedestrian traffic only and footways likely to be overridden by no more than occasional vehicular traffic.

The Standard states that:

'Naturally occurring sand from the quaternary geological series or sea dredged sands selected and graded according to the [applications given above] should be used. Other material and crushed rock fines should only be used for category IV applications'

Wales in such applications. One contractor reported in discussions that SQS can form a better platform than standard marine sand as it offers better compaction to form a firmer base. This is likely to be due to the well graded nature of the SQS compared to the relatively single sized marine sand.

To determine the effectiveness of the SQS as bedding sand a trial was undertaken at the premises of Gerald Davies Ltd. in Margam, near Port Talbot.

Three block paved parking bays were constructed using sharp building sand meeting the grading envelope, SQS with the <75 µm fraction removed and unseparated SQS. The advantage with this trial is that the bays are used daily, and therefore an assessment of performance in a live environment was obtained.

Preparation of the parking bays commenced in early December 2003, with construction of the control bay and the SQS bay undertaken on December 23rd 2003.

Construction of the >75 μm SQS bay was undertaken in late January 2004.

Plate 19 is an image of the progress of the parking bays on December 15, 2003, with the areas defined and prepared awaiting the arrival of the bedding sand.

Plate 19 Block paving bedding sand trial (under construction

Construction thickness

The bays were constructed in general accordance with Application Guide 26 (11), with parking bays laid out with kerbstones as indicated in the above figure. A sub-base was constructed using coarse crushed rock fill, which was compacted using a vibrating plate.

Control sand

The control sand section was laid on the afternoon of December 23rd 2003 to a depth of 30 mm, as per the guidance in AG26 (11). The sand was then compacted using a vibrating plate. Concrete pavers measuring 50 mm deep were laid directly on to the sand layer in sets of two, laid longitudinally and laterally as shown in Plate 20.

Plate 20 Pavers being laid over SQS

The SQS was laid in the middle bay on the afternoon of December 23rd 2003 to a depth of 30 mm. An attempt at passing the vibrating plate over the material failed, possibly due to the material being relatively wet. The operatives reported that the material was sticking to the bottom of the plate and being pushed forward rather than compacting. From previous experience in using this material, the operative suggested that the material compacted better than general building sand and formed a harder base, but that moisture control was critical. As a well graded material, it could well be expected that the material will achieve good particle interlock, but the strength analysis presented in Section 2.5 suggests that strength is significantly decreased when the material is wetted beyond the optimum. As previously, the pavers were laid directly onto the sand base layer as shown in Plate 20.

Having laid both the control sand section and the SQS section, a vibrating plate was run over the pavers to improve compaction as shown in Plate 21. Typically, kiln dried sand is used to fill the joints between the pavers following compaction to reduce any movement of the pavers which may cause long term failure of the parking bay. At the time the pavers were laid, it was considered that it was too wet for the sand to be brushed in, and this activity was carried out at a later date.

Plate 21 SQS and control sand bays being compacted using vibrating plate

> 75 μm washed SQS

Following receipt of the washed sand from Hanson, the final bay was laid using the same process as described above on January 23rd 2004. As with the control sand, it was possible to compact the sand using a vibrating plate prior to laying the pavers.

The bays are used by cars and light vehicles every working day, equivalent to category III usage as defined by BS7533 (10) Regular monitoring visits were undertaken to visually assess the condition of the bays during the course of the project, with all three performing well, with no visible differences between the bays.

Measurement of the levels after ten months of use indicate that all three bays including the kerbs have settled, although there was no obvious drop in levels or rutting visible except on one corner of Bay 1, the control sand bay. A total of 40 measurements were taken in each bay with the largest average and single downward movement recorded in Bay 1 of 3.13 and 5.00 mm respectively.

Bay 2, containing unseparated SQS had an average downward movement of 2.05 mm with Bay 3, the >75 μm bay performing marginally better with an average downward movement of 1.83 mm.

The results of the monitoring clearly indicate the SQS is a suitable material for use in this application, with both the separated and unseparated material outperforming the control marine sand. As the performance of the unseparated material was so near to that of the washed SQS, it is considered that with adequate moisture control there would be no requirement for additional processing and that the unseparated SQS could be used..

Box 8 Measurement of levels

Following construction of the block paving beds, a total of 128 optical levels were taken on the pavers, comprising eight levels taken on the concrete kerbing around the bays, and 120 levels on the bays, i.e. 40 per car parking bay. If the bays were to fail, it is likely that the failure would occur along the line that vehicles would take whilst parking, and specifically in the areas where tyres will be acting as points of pressure for long periods whilst parked. The survey points for the bays were therefore concentrated around these areas. A set of comparable level data was taken in the final stages of this project, as detailed above.

3.2.5 Cement extender

Indicative tests were carried out by Environmental and Industrial Evaluations (E&IE) to determine whether SQS, and specifically the filler fraction, could be used as a cement replacement or cement extender. The investigation of the chemical and physical properties of the sample was determined over a period of six months between May and October 2003 using the methods listed in Box 9.

From the chemical and physical analyses it was determined that the fine fraction of the SQS can be used

---

Box 9 Testing undertaken

- Mortar prisms were produced and tested over a period of 90 days in accordance with BS: EN 196 Part 1:1995 (12).

- Chemical analysis was carried out by drying and grinding the material samples, preparing them using lithium metaborate and testing by an Induced Coupled Plasma (ICP-OES) system.

- Test samples were prepared and tested for soundness over 24 hours using Le Chatelier apparatus in accordance with BS EN 196-3:1995 (13).

- Pozzolanicity was tested in accordance with BS EN 196-5:1995 (14).

- The determination of free lime, loss on ignition, insoluble residue and sulphate was carried out in accordance with BS EN 196-2:1995 (15). The Na_2O equivalent was calculated using the method set out within the Standard.

- The EPA 1312 Leach Extraction Test (16) was adopted, and carried out using the modification of a ratio of 2:1 which was 100ml of water to 50gms of material sample.

---

as a component of a cement substitute or concrete extender, subject to the requirements of the end user and availability of other materials that will make up the cement substitute.

The leachate results showed a significant increase in lime leaching from the mortar samples when the SQS is added. This could result in a problem of efflorescence on concrete products that are made incorporating this material. It was also noted that in most cases the potassium and sodium concentrations are much lower than that of Ordinary Portland Cement (OPC). As both sodium and potassium are detrimental, it is preferable to have as low a concentration as possible.

The SQS gave a positive result for pozzolanicity, but contains a very high insoluble residue, therefore the main function of the material would be for it to act as a filler and this would limit the quantity used in a cement substitute.

A recommendation of E&IE's test report was that further work be undertaken on the effects of the calcium, potassium and sodium that could be changing the structure of the concrete. A further recommendation was that the changes in the compounds that may be taking place when using these materials should be investigated by x-ray diffraction (XRD).

Whilst it would appear that the material could be used in limited quantities as filler in a cement substitute, it was unclear as to whether potential quantities that could be used would warrant additional testing to be carried out. It was also unclear whether it would be practical for the quarry to undertake the processing required to separate the filler from the SQS and subsequently dry the material prior to inclusion with the cement mix. If these issues were resolved, further testing could be undertaken.

3.3 Landscaping applications

3.3.1 Manufactured topsoil

Previous work undertaken by Harper Adams College (17) has indicated that a siltstone / sandstone quarry waste and composted green waste can be used to manufacture a landscaping and growing medium, although additional fertiliser would be required.

The relevant British Standard, BS 3882:1994 – Specification for Topsoil (18), specifies requirements for topsoil by establishing three grades of material:

- Premium grade.

- General-purpose grade.

- Economy grade.

There are six requirements, listed below, that must be met for each grade of topsoil, with the requirements becoming increasingly stringent from economy to premium grade.

- Textural classification.

- Maximum stone content.

- pH value.

- Nutrient content.

- Loss on ignition.

- Exchangeable sodium percentage.

Given the likelihood of any manufactured soil at least initially, having to be categorised as a general purpose grade, the physical and textural requirements for this grade are presented in Figure 8 and Table 9.

Initial work by Harper Adams College (17) suggests that by using a 70:30 blend by volume of either the filler fraction or unseparated SQS and suitable organic material, the textural classification and stone size requirements of general-purpose grade topsoil will be achieved. The results suggest that the use of the filler fraction would produce a superior topsoil compared to one manufactured with unseparated SQS.

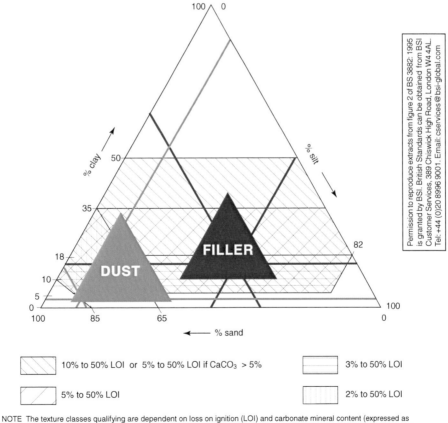

10% to 50% LOI or 5% to 50% LOI if CaCO₃ > 5%

3% to 50% LOI

5% to 50% LOI

2% to 50% LOI

NOTE The texture classes qualifying are dependent on loss on ignition (LOI) and carbonate mineral content (expressed as calcium carbonate) because of the structure modifying effects of these components. No soil has LOI > 50% *(m/m)*. General purpose grade is applicable to soils whose LOI falls within the appropriate shaded area. The procedure for the estimation of calcium carbonate is described in Annex P.

Figure 8 Topsoil standard
(SQS and filler fraction compared to topsoil standard taken from BS3882:1994)

Table 9 Physical requirements for a general grade topsoil

Property	Permitted level
Textural classification	See Figure 8
Maximum stone content % (m/m)	
Stone size:	
> 2 mm	60
> 20 mm	30
> 50 mm	10
Loss on ignition % (m/m)	See Figure 8

In addition to the physical and textural requirements for general-purpose grade topsoil, there are a number of chemical and nutrient requirements that must also be met, which are summarised in Table 10.

Table 10 Chemical and nutrient requirements for a Premium and General grade topsoil

Property	Permitted level
pH value (Premium grade)	5.5 to 7.8
pH value (General grade)	5.0 to 8.2
Nutrient content (both Premium and General grade)	
P index min.	2 ($\geq$16 mg/l)
K index min.	2 ($\geq$121 mg/l)
Mg index min.	1 ($\geq$26 mg/l)
N % (m/m) min.	0.2
Exchangeable sodium percentage (ESP) %	< 15

As SQS is essentially an inert material, it would be unable to supply the required nutrients or the organic fraction to meet the requirements of general purpose grade topsoil, and so careful selection of an organic fraction is required.

Trials

In order to establish whether local material, when mixed with an organic fraction could support grass growth, six test beds were constructed at the Geoenvironmental Research Park, near Port Talbot. This enabled vegetation growth to be quantified on two test bed controls (high fertility and low fertility) and four manufactured soil test beds, as detailed below.

Mix design

Four of the six test beds comprised a 2:1 mineral to organic mix ratio by volume, a decision based on work undertaken previously by Harper Adams College, and on the ease of mixing. Green waste compost was sourced from Swansea

City Council who compost parks and garden waste from the Neath Port Talbot CBC area. Whilst other organic mixes have been used on other sites, such as paper and tannery waste, it is considered that green waste compost is a common material found in most areas of the UK and, in due course, will potentially become widely available as a result of the EC Landfill Directive (19). The Landfill Directive imposes limits on the quantity of biodegradable municipal waste (e.g. garden clippings, vegetable waste) that can be sent to landfill, and many local authorities now compost such material to satisfy the obligations of the Directive. As the limits become increasingly stringent, it is likely that more and more local authorities will adopt a similar approach.

Controls

The fifth test bed was a control bed divided longitudinally into a natural topsoil material and a recycled soil manufactured locally from subsoil and construction, demolition and excavation waste (CD&EW); in this manner growth will be compared between different materials.

It is recognised that on a highway scheme for example, high quality topsoil would rarely be used, and growth on this material is likely to represent an artificially high control comparison. For this reason, a sixth bed was constructed and divided into SQS and filler only, i.e. no organic material, to demonstrate the effect of the addition of the organic fraction as a growing medium. A plan of the test beds is shown on Figure 9.

Construction

The test beds were approximately 3.0 m square, and 450 mm high, with the material placed to a depth of 250 mm and lightly compacted using a tamper board. To ensure that rabbits were prevented from gaining access to the beds, appropriate stock proof fencing surrounded the test area, as shown in Plate 23.

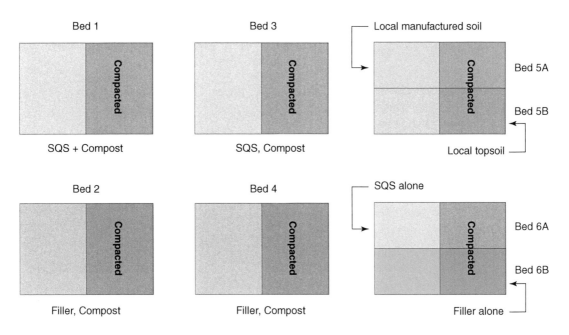

Bed 1

Compacted

SQS + Compost

Bed 3

Compacted

SQS, Compost

Local manufactured soil

Compacted

Bed 5A

Bed 5B

Local topsoil

Bed 2

Compacted

Filler, Compost

Bed 4

Compacted

Filler, Compost

SQS alone

Compacted

Bed 6A

Bed 6B

Filler alone

Figure 9 Layout of test beds

Box 11 Requirements of Landfill Directive

The Landfill Directive requires local authorities to reduce the quantity of biodegradable municipal waste landfilled to:

- 75% of 1995 levels by 2010.

- 50% of 1995 levels by 2013.

- 35% of 1995 levels by 2020.

Other requirements of Directive

There is a requirement to increase the rate of composting and recycling as follows

- 25% by 2005.

- 30% by 2010.

- 33% by 2015.

Other requirements of the Directive include a ban on co-disposal of waste, a ban on the landfill of whole tyres from July 2004 and on shredded tyres from 2006.

Plate 22 Loading Bed 2 with filler and compost mix

Plate 23 Completed test beds surrounded by stock proof fencing

Compaction

Physical properties can be just as important as the nutrient content in promoting vegetation growth. It was decided that rather than try to achieve exact densities in the beds, it would be preferable to leave one half of each bed 'as is', i.e. compacted by walking over a tamper board, as shown in Plate 24, and to mechanically compact the other half, as shown in Plate 25. Compaction was achieved using a 3 kW, 60 kg Wacker (model VP1B5A). Four passes of the Wacker were used on each of the compacted beds for consistency.

Plate 24 Compacting test beds using boards

Plate 25 Compaction of one half of test bed using wacker plate

In-situ density measurements were undertaken (sand replacement method in accordance with, BS 1377-9:1990) (20) in each test bed, with the measured densities presented in Table 11.

In most cases good levels of compaction were achieved using the Wacker plate. The SQS and compost mix (Bed 1 and Bed 3) compacts reasonably consistently

Plate 26 Measurement of compaction using sand replacement method

(within 10 %), with even greater compaction of SQS alone (Bed 6A).

Compaction of the filler material (Bed 6B) and the filler and compost beds (Bed 2 and Bed 4) proved difficult, possibly due to the fineness of the material, resulting in a general lack of void space, particularly in the filler only bed (Bed 6B). It was reported that the filler was very soft and 'springy' and difficult to compact consistently. This is a sign of very low air voids and the build up of positive pore pressures, and might be a result of the material being compacted at a moisture content above optimum. The higher compaction recorded was actually in an area that had been walked on and gave higher compaction readings than the mechanically compacted section. It is unclear why this might be the case, although it is possible that the moisture content of the filler was dry of optimum.

The manufactured and natural soils also compacted relatively well, with an increase in bulk density of over 10%, in the natural topsoil, again likely to be due to the well graded nature of the materials.

Seeding and fertiliser

Each bed was sown with a standard Department of Transport Pro85 grass and clover (5%) mix at a rate of 10 g/m^2, i.e. 90 g per test bed, in accordance with the suppliers instructions. This mix is designed for road verges and it is considered that the addition of clover may assist in the long term performance of the soil as the clover helps to fix atmospheric nitrogen.

Monitoring

Monitoring was undertaken on a weekly basis by the resident TRL staff at the GRP. This included an assessment of grass growth using a modified Braun-Blanquet scale and also a digital photographic record of vegetation performance.

Table 11 Bulk densities in test beds prior to and following compaction

Bed ID	Bed composition	Bulk density (Mg m-3)	Dry density (Mg m-3)	Moisture content (%)	Change in bulk density (%)
B1 - L	SQS & green waste compost	1.30	1.09	19.5	
B1 - H		1.47	1.25	17.8	+12.8
B2 - L	Filler & green waste compost	1.11	0.91	21.4	
B2 - H		1.15	0.88	30.7	+4.2
B3 - L	SQS & green waste compost	1.25	1.14	17.7	
B3 - H		1.37	1.06	20.3	+9.6
B4 - L	Filler & green waste compost	1.19	0.90	22.6	
B4 - H		1.14	0.97	26.3	-4.0
B5A - L	Locally manufactured soil	1.36	1.17	15.5	
B5A - H		1.45	1.23	17.4	+6.8
B5B - L	Local natural topsoil	1.09	0.92	17.8	
B5B - H		1.21	0.94	27.6	+10.7
B6A - L	SQS alone	1.49	1.43	3.9	
B6A - H		1.75	1.66	5.1	+17.4
B6B - L	Filler alone	1.36	1.21	12.3	
B6B - H		1.16	1.06	9.3	-14.6

L = Low compaction (i.e. compacted by foot).

H = Higher compaction (Wacker plate used).

Analysis of the manufactured soil mixes and of the topsoil for comparison with the British Standard was undertaken at the beginning of the monitoring period. Trial pits were excavated from the test beds on October 28th to take samples for nutrient analysis. Three holes were excavated in Beds 1 to 4 and a composite sample taken. Two holes were excavated in Beds 5A and 5B due to the smaller size, and a composite sample also taken.

The nutrient requirements of general purpose topsoil are presented in Table 12, taken from BS3882.

Table 12 Nutrient concentration classification (from BS3882)

Index	Concentration of extractable elements in milligrams per litre of soil		
	P	K	Mg
0	0 – 9	0 – 60	0 – 25
1	10 – 15	61 – 120	26 – 50
2	16 – 25	121 – 240	51 – 100
3	26 – 45	241 – 400	101 – 175
4	46 – 70	401 – 600	176 – 250
5	71 – 100	601 – 900	251 – 350
6	101 – 140	901 – 1500	351 – 600
7	141 – 200	1501 – 2400	601 – 1000
8	201 – 280	2401 – 3600	1001 – 1500
9	Over 280	Over 3600	Over 1500

The minimum nutrient contents for both premium and general purpose topsoil are to achieve an Index value of 2 for both phosphorous and potassium and an Index value of 1 for magnesium. A comparison of the results of chemical analysis with the standard above is presented in Table 13.

Table 13 indicates that when mixed with compost, both the SQS and filler can achieve the majority of the requirements of the British Standard for topsoil, in some cases outperforming both the locally manufactured topsoil and natural topsoil.

None of the soils, including the natural topsoil meet the minimum requirement of 0.2% nitrogen, although the SQS and compost blend was the nearest to reaching the target at 0.16%. The proportion of compost could be increased in order to reach the figure, or some kind of fertiliser could be added to reach the levels of nitrogen required. Unless a particularly high fertility soil was required, it is questionable whether this would really be necessary.

With the exception of nitrogen, both of the soils manufactured from SQS and compost and filler and compost meet the requirements for nutrients, pH, loss on ignition and exchangeable sodium. Both mixes also meet the more stringent premium grade targets for loss on ignition (5 – 50%) and exchangeable sodium (<10%), although only the natural topsoil would meet the premium grade targets for pH (5.5 – 7.8).

Table 13 Results of chemical analysis

Analyte	Units	General purpose target	SQS and compost	Nat. topsoil	Local recycled soil	Filler and compost	Compost
Calcium (MAFF extract)	mg/l	–	2900	4100	3500	1900	4100
Magnesium (MAFF extract)	mg/l	–	420	260	140	350	590
Extractable magnesium	BS index	≥1	6	5	3	5	6
Phosphorus (extractable)	mg/l	–	86	62	78	26	110
Extractable phosphorous	BS index	≥2	5	4	5	3	6
Potassium (MAFF extract)	mg/l	–	1300	660	110	600	2500
Extractable potassium	BS index	≥2	6	5	1	4	8
Sodium exchangeable	%	<15	4.31	3.62	2.76	3.94	5.95
EC (CaSO4 extract)	µS/cm	*	2400	2300	2100	2200	3300
Loss on ignition	%	5–50%**	7.3	11	2	5.7	52
Specific gravity	Mg/m-3	–	2.26	2.00	2.28	1.97	1.13
pH	pH units	5.0 – 8.2	8.1	7.4	8.1	8.1	7.9
Total kjeldahl nitrogen	%	0.2%	0.16	0.13	0.14	0.1	0.58

* *The exchangeable sodium percentage need only be calculated if the EC is greater than 2800 µS/cm.*

** *Without further sedimentation analysis the exact loss on ignition required cannot be determined, however, based on the sand and silt content, it is likely that 5 – 50% would be appropriate. This is also the premium grade classification.*

The worst performing material overall, not including the mineral only beds, is the local recycled soil which in addition to failing to meet the requirements for nitrogen, also failed to meet the general purpose grade requirements for potassium and recorded only 2% loss on ignition (LoI). BS3882 (18) specifies LoI values depending on the blend of sands, clays and silts with the best blend of particle sizes having an allowable range of 2% to 50%, but for the worst blend, the LoI must fall between 10% and 50%. The sand content of 36% for the recycled soil indicates that at best it would require a minimum LoI of 3%.

Results

Six composite samples were taken from the test beds at the end of the trial to assess the effect of vegetation establishment on the various soils. Samples were taken by excavating three holes in each test bed to the base of the soil and taking a sample from the length of the excavation. The three samples were placed in a bucket and mixed thoroughly before placing in a sample container for laboratory analysis. For Bed 5 which is split into two, the same procedure was applied only using two samples from each of the two beds. Samples were not taken from Bed 6. The results of the analysis are presented in Table 14.

Table 14 Results of chemical analysis of test beds at end of trial

Analyte	Units	General purpose target	SQS compost Bed 1	SQS compost Bed 3	Filler compost Bed 2	Filler compost Bed 4	Man. topsoil Bed 5A	Nat. topsoil Bed 5B
Magnesium (MAFF extract)	mg/l	–	420	740	590	540	170	290
Extractable magnesium	BS Index	≥1	6	7	6	6	3	4
Phosphorus (extractable)	mg/l	–	89	64	65	67	57	67
Extractable phosphorous	BS Index	≥2	5	4	4	4	4	4
Potassium (MAFF extract)	mg/l	–	800	410	1400	1200	280	680
Extractable potassium	BS Index	≥2	5	4	6	6	3	5
EC (CaSO4 extract)	µS/cm	*	1700	1700	2000	1700	1600	1700
Loss on ignition	%	5–50%**	9.6	10	8.2	7.8	9	15
Specific gravity	Mg/mn	–	2.41	2.21	2.05	2.15	2.36	2.03
pH	pH units	5.0 – 8.2	7.9	7.8	7.7	7.8	7.9	7.9
Total kjeldahl nitrogen	%	0.2%	0.12	0.17	0.15	0.36	0.19	0.24

* *The exchangeable sodium percentage need only be calculated if the EC is greater than 2800 µS/cm.*

** *Without further sedimentation analysis the exact loss on ignition required cannot be determined, however, based on the sand and silt content, it is likely that 5 – 50% would be appropriate. This is also the premium grade classification.*

After 22 weeks since seeding, it can be seen that all of the soils comfortably exceed the nutrient requirements and loss on ignition requirements, with all soils also comfortably meeting the pH requirements, with both filler and compost beds and one of the two SQS and compost beds just meeting the more stringent Premium grade classification. The locally manufactured topsoil bed is again the poorest performing with generally lower nutrients than the natural or manufactured soils, with exception of phosphorous which were similar for all mixes.

The loss on ignition has improved for all soils as a result of increased carbon from the root growth and micro-organisms that have colonised the soil, but markedly for the locally manufactured soil which has shown an improvement in a number of areas.

Vegetation establishment

It would have been impractical to attempt to undertake a trial in the timescale available that assessed a large number of admixtures at various mix proportions. The purpose of this limited trial was to demonstrate whether or not the material can be used to successfully grow grass using a widely available organic fraction at a proportion that has been demonstrated to have been successful on similar trials previously. The results of the trial are presented below.

Overall results show that with the exception of Bed 6, which contains SQS and Filler alone, all beds showed the ability to establish vegetation at a reasonable rate and sustain vegetation successfully. Specific discussion of vegetation growth is presented below.

Figure 10 presents the average grass growth on the test beds, based on the observations of the TRL staff at the GEP using the Blaun-Blanquet scale for grass vegetation cover. As the upper category of the scale is 76 to 100% cover, it appears the maximum 'average' achievable is 88%. Beds 1 and 3 contain SQS mixed with a locally sourced Green Waste Compost (GWC), and achieved an estimated 50% average vegetation cover by weeks 10 and 5 respectively. Despite taking longer than Bed 3 to reach 50% cover, Bed 1 attained full cover by week 17 whilst Bed 3 took a further 4 weeks to reach this stage.

Beds 2 and 4 contain the filler fraction of SQS mixed with GWC and were slower to vegetate than the SQS and GWC beds. Bed 2 attained an estimated 50% average cover by week 14 following a significant burst of growth which saw coverage increased from 25% on week 11 and managed a maximum estimated cover of 91% by the end of the final week of the trial. Bed 4 reached 50 % average cover by week 10 and followed to reach 100% cover on the week preceding the end of the trial (week 22).

Overall, the performance of the soils manufactured from both SQS and filler is reasonably similar. Three out of the four beds attained full vegetation cover at least one week before the termination of the trial and all beds managed an average estimated cover of 80% between 13 and 7 weeks before completion. As is evident from Figure 10, although all beds attained a reasonable vegetation cover, SQS with compost beds are faster to vegetate initially; this may simply be due to the coarser nature of the material resulting in the availability of larger pore spaces to trap moisture and allow for root development than is found in the finer grained filler with

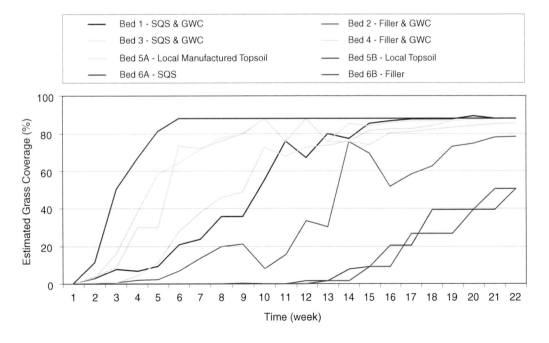

Figure 10 Average grass growth on test beds

compost beds. Rate of vegetation growth early on in the trial proved no indication of later vegetation rate, as demonstrated by Bed 2.

The natural topsoil (Bed 5B) was the most successful of all the test beds in terms of initial vegetation cover, reaching 50% cover by weeks 3, 80% cover by week 5 and 100% cover by week 6 of the trial. Along with Bed 3 (SQS and GWC), the locally produced soil (Bed 5A) also established quickly, reaching 50% cover by week 6. Whilst the growth generally matched that of Bed 3, by week 14 of the trial both Bed 1 and Bed 4 had matched the average cover and along with Bed 3 outperformed this soil for the remainder of the trial. By the end of the trial the soil had not surpassed 97% cover. The initial good performance of both the natural topsoil and locally produced soil is not unexpected as they contain a natural seed bank resulting in increased vegetation cover and faster germination times. The disadvantage to this natural seed bank however, is that both soils contained numerous weeds. It must also be noted that, although, vegetation was fast to establish on the locally manufactured soil, it did not reach the size nor volume encountered in the other vegetated beds as shown in Figure 12. Furthermore, yellowing of the vegetation was observed in Bed 5 (Figure 10). This is indicative of a lack of nutrients, in particular nitrates, in these soils. Vegetation in beds 1 to 4 displayed no such discoloration.

As is the case with Bed 5, Bed 6 is divided into two sections. Section 6A contains SQS alone and section 6B contains filler alone. These bare materials, without the benefit of GWC, proved to be slow to promote vegetation growth. Halfway through the trial (week 11), Bed 6 had not attained 1% estimated vegetation cover. Following an extended wet period, however, Bed 6 started to vegetate at a more rapid pace. From week 13 onwards, grass cover increased steadily to a maximum estimated cover of 63%.

Bed 5A (local manufactured soil) and Bed 5B (natural topsoil)

Figure 11 Vegetation establishment on Bed 5

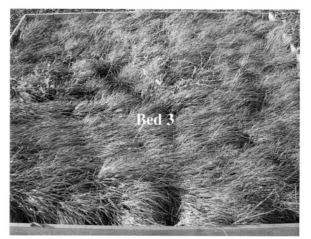

Bed 3 (SQS and GWC)

Figure 12 Vegetation establishment on Beds 3

The establishment of vegetation on all beds around the midpoint and at the end of the trial is shown in Figure 13 and Figure 14.

Effect of compaction on vegetation establishment

Despite initial increased vegetation coverage of the non-compacted sections of Beds 1 and 3, as of week 10 (midway through the trial) both sections (compacted and non-compacted) attained similar cover.

In comparison to Beds 1 and 3, it initially appeared that in Beds 2 and 4 the compacted sections were initially more successfully covered with vegetation than the non-compacted sections. A density test carried out on Bed 4, however, showed that the area acted on by the whacker plate was less compacted that that on which the whacker plate was not used.

Bed 5A displays similar behaviour to Beds 1 and 3 in that compaction resulted in an initial lower rate of vegetation cover. This was overcome by week 6 from which time the rate of spread, for both the compacted and non-compacted sections, was similar. In the case of Bed 5B, compaction of the topsoil had no effect on the rate of spread of vegetation.

The degree of compaction of the materials is only relevant to vegetation growth in as much as it affects the initial rate of germination and spread. Following a brief period of growth, however, compacted and non-compacted sections behave in a similar fashion. This behaviour is well demonstrated by Bed 1, as shown in Figure 15.

3.3.2 SQS for use in playing fields drainage

An enquiry was made to TRL from Neath Port Talbot CB Council regarding the potential use of SQS in place of marine dredged sand to improve the drainage

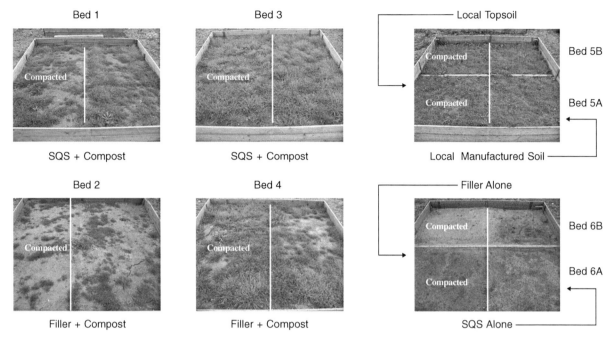

Note that 'compacted' refer to the areas where mechanical compaction was used, not the degree of compaction

Figure 13 Test beds at Week 12

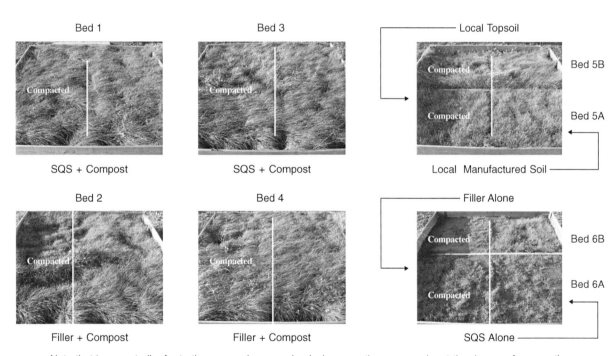

Note that 'compacted' refer to the areas where mechanical compaction was used, not the degree of compaction

Figure 14 Test beds at Week 23

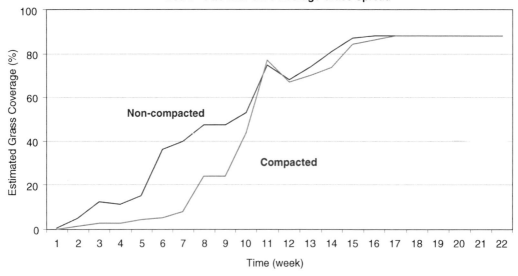

Figure 15 Effect of compaction on vegetation establishment

characteristics of two playing fields in the county (Redfield Playing Field and Tudor Park Playing Field). Calculations carried out based on the control sand information, SQS and information provided on the topsoil suggest that the addition of SQS would not significantly improve the drainage, but that if the filler was removed the material would be appropriate. Particle size distribution analysis of the playing field soils undertaken by Babtie revealed that 68.4% (Redfield) and 63% (Tudor Park) of the playing field soils were sand-sized. On the advice of external consultants it was suggested that the proportion should be raised to 75% to improve drainage, yet retain sufficient organic material to sustain growth.

Samples of playing field soil from Redfield, marine sand, SQS and >75 μm SQS were sent to Fugro laboratories in Hemel Hempstead for permeability testing using a constant head permeameter cell. Both the topsoil and the playing field sand were found to be too fine to be analysed using by the standard permeameter method and were analysed using a Tri-axial cell method. The results of the testing are presented in Table 15.

Table 15 Results of permeability testing

Material	Coefficient of permeability (m/s)
Topsoil	2.8×10^{-7}
Control sand	4.52×10^{-3}
>75μm SQS	3.10×10^{-3}
Unseparated SQS	5.50×10^{-9}

The testing clearly demonstrates that SQS would be unsuitable as a drainage improver as it actually has a permeability two orders of magnitude lower than the topsoil. This is solely due to the high fines content.

With the filler removed, however, the material would form an excellent drainage improver. Whilst the permeability is not quite as high as the control marine sand, it should be noted that permeability is measured on a logarithmic scale, and therefore the difference in permeability will be effectively indistinguishable. The improvement in permeability of the SQS with the filler removed can clearly be seen as it is 6 orders of magnitude higher than the unseparated SQS.

4 Summary

Sandstone quarry sand (SQS) is produced by the crushing and screening of Pennant sandstone in five quarries in South Wales. The crushed rock represents a valuable resource as an aggregate with excellent skid resistance properties. However, the generation of the crushed rock results in the production of large quantities of fine sand sized material, known as SQS.

The material is very well graded from a maximum grain size slightly larger than 3.5 mm to a clay fraction, with around 15 – 20% of the material smaller than 75 μm, known as 'filler' or 'fines'. It is very consistent in grading and other properties. Precise levels of production are difficult to estimate, but a report prepared by Arup for the Aggregates Levy Sustainability Fund for Wales (ALSFW) reports that approximately 0.9 million tonnes of SQS were produced in 2001, based on 35% of the total of 2.64 million tonnes sandstone produced in the South Wales Regional Aggregate Working Party area, the majority of which will have been produced in the South Wales coalfield region.

The material is a charcoal grey colour and its well graded nature allows compaction to a high density and low air voids. The potential for the fines to absorb water is a significant issue with the material as whilst the material exhibits excellent strength at optimum moisture content, the strength decreases dramatically when wet of optimum. However, the material can be mixed with cement to form a versatile material.

Moisture content is very important with much lower moisture recorded in the production material with an average of around 3% compared to the stockpiled material which has an average of around 10% moisture.

This document aims to provide the reader with technical information on the material, to highlight applications that have been or are currently in use, and to disseminate the new applications that have been trialled. The aim is to encourage greater use of this valuable and versatile material.

Guidance is provided for clients, specifiers and contractors who may consider using SQS and for planning authorities who may receive an application where the use of SQS is proposed. The document should be of interest to local and national government, infrastructure owners and operators, contractors, designers and the research community.

Applications

A number of applications have been identified that would be suitable for the material which can be broadly broken down into Engineering, Construction and Landscaping categories.

Engineering

The material has successfully been used as an admixture to bentonite to form part of an impervious layer for constructing landfills. Whilst this is a high volume market, demand is infrequent. The material is suitable for use as engineered fill for a variety of applications, but this is a low value market and hence there will be many other competing materials, with transport costs likely to be the deciding factor in its use.

The material is liable to heave if exposed to prolonged frost, so it cannot be used for unbound applications such as road sub-base where resistance to frost is important. It would be suitable if combined with other materials, washed to remove the fines or stabilised with cement. Testing undertaken showed that the addition of 4% OPC by volume would produce suitable strengths required to meet the cement bound material (CBM1) specifications for road sub-base construction.

In less critical applications such as cycle paths or footways, it is possible to utilise the material, and for

this reason a cycle path trial was constructed at Afan Argoed Country Park near Port Talbot. The trial consisted of two sections; one a flat 60 metre long section and another on tight bend around 11 metres long on the outside. The flat section was divided into three 20 metre long sections to assess the performance of unbound SQS, SQS with OPC and a section with an underlying scalpings layer. As the bend was subject to heavy braking, this area was mixed with approximately 4% OPC. All of the areas are performing well eight months after construction, with the unbound section performing the best overall in terms of appearance and general resistance to wear. This would also be the least expensive construction option. The rangers in Afan Argoed Country Park are delighted with the performance of the material.

As a result of the success of this trial, SQS was used for construction of a BMX track at Britton Ferry in November 2004.

Construction

The material has been successfully used in a variety of construction applications including concrete building blocks, where typical 7N/mm^2 blocks are successfully manufactured using SQS. It is understood that 10% of 6 mm aggregate is added to the mix to prevent balling with the cost savings associated with the use of SQS more than outweighing the cost of the 6 mm aggregate.

Structural C30 concrete is currently manufactured by Hanson Aggregates using around 12% SQS. At present this is the maximum economic percentage, although if a use could be found for the filler, this percentage could be increased significantly.

The potential for SQS fines to be used as a cement replacement or extender was examined. It was found that there would be some potential as a cement extender. However, due to operational issues in separating and drying the fines, further research has not been pursued at this stage.

Another trial involved the use of the material as bedding sand for block paving and slabs. The material does not meet the specifications required due to the high percentage of fines with the potential for the material to heave in frost conditions. It is understood, however, that the specification is occasionally overlooked, and that the material can in fact perform better than the specified material as its well graded nature causes it to compact better and produce a firmer base. It should be noted that the material needs to be close to the OMC for this to be the case.

A trial was carried out where three parking bays were constructed using SQS, control material and SQS with the fines removed. The latter material met the specifications. After ten months use, there did not appear to be any significant difference in appearance between any of the three bays, with both the >75 μm SQS and unseparated SQS outperforming the control marine sand. However, the trial was undertaken in a coastal location and the application may be less suitable where severe or prolonged frosts are more common.

Landscaping applications

The potential for the material to be used as a mineral base for a manufactured soil was examined. It was decided to mix SQS at a ratio of 2:1 by volume with green waste compost, as this is likely to be a widely available product as a result of the increased local authority composting. Six 3 m by 3 m test beds were constructed at the Geoenvironmental Research Park comprising SQS and compost (2 beds), filler and compost (2 beds), natural topsoil and a soil manufactured from subsoil and construction, demolition and excavation waste (1 bed divided into 2) and a bed with SQS and filler only (1 bed divided into 2).

The beds were compacted by foot on one side and using a mechanical compactor on the other with *in-situ* measurements of density recorded. The plots were then sown with Department of Transport grass seed mix. The results demonstrate that SQS and green waste compost in particular provide a suitable growing medium, with nearly all of the nutrient requirements of the British Standard for topsoil comfortably met by the mixes. The filler and compost also provided good growth, but was slower to establish vegetation that the SQS and compost mix and was more difficult to handle and compact.

Another potentially high volume use for SQS would be as a drainage improver for playing fields. This idea was investigated following an enquiry from Neath Port Talbot CBC, who were planning to import around 5,000 tonnes of sand to be mixed with topsoil on a playing field. Samples of the topsoil, control sand, >75 μm SQS and unseparated SQS were sent for permeameter testing. It was found that the unseparated SQS had a very low permeability at 5.50×10-9, which is in fact two orders of magnitude lower than the topsoil.

Removal of the filler, increases the permeability of the SQS by six orders of magnitude to 3.1×10-3 which is effectively inseparable to the control sand's permeability of 4.52×10-3. With the filler removed, therefore, the SQS would make an ideal drainage improver.

Advantages of using sandstone quarry sand

Sandstone quarry sand is a versatile material, available in the valleys and adjacent areas of South Wales, plus other parts of the UK and beyond. It is very consistent in properties and capable of a wide variety of applications, as detailed above. Use of this material can reduce the demand for land won or marine dredged sand and gravel, thus preserving valuable natural resources. It also ensures that the material is being used constructively, rather than accumulating in stockpiles in the quarries or being used for low-value end uses. Use of the material, where appropriate, will therefore contribute to sustainable development and should be encouraged.

This Design Guide describes applications for which the material is suitable for use in South Wales. However, similar sandstone in other parts of the UK and elsewhere are also quarried for high skid resistance aggregates, resulting in the production of similar sandstone quarry sand. Many of the applications described may therefore also be suitable in these other areas.

5   References

1 **Welsh Assembly Government.** *Minerals Planning Policy (Wales)*. Minerals Technical Advice Note (Wales) 1: Aggregates. March 2004. ISBN 07504 3314 0.

2 **Arup for Aggregates Levy Sustainability Fund for Wales (2003)**. *Improving the information base on secondary minerals / C&D waste for use as aggregates in Wales*. Draft Final Report, November 2003.

3 **Smith G N (1978)**. *Elements of soil mechanics for civil and mining engineers*. Fourth Edition. Crosby Lockwood Staples. ISBN 0258971053.

4 **British Standards Institution (1990)**. *Methods of test for - soils for civil engineering purposes. Part 2: Classification tests*. BS1377-2:1990. London: British Standards Institution.

5 **British Standards Institution (1981)**. *Code of Practice for site investigations*. BS5930:1981. London: British Standards Institution.

6 **Highways Agency, Scottish Office Development Department, Welsh Office and the Department of the Environment for Northern Ireland (2001)**. Manual of Contract Documents for Highway Works (MCHW 1). London: The Stationery Office.

Volume 1: Specification for Highway Works (May 2001).

7 **British Standards Institution (1990)**. *Methods of test for - soils for civil engineering purposes. Part 4: Compaction related tests*. BS1377-4:1990. London: British Standards Institution.

8 **British Standards Institution (1989)**. *Testing aggregates. Part 4: Methods for determination of frost heave.* BS812-4:1989. London: British Standards Institution.

9 **British Standards Institution (1990)**. *Part 2: Methods of test for cement stabilised and lime stabilised materials.* BS1924:1990. London: British Standards Institution.

10 **British Standards Institution (1997)**. *Pavements constructed with clay, natural stone or concrete pavers. Part 3: Code of Practice for laying precast concrete paving blocks and clay pavers for flexible pavements.* BS 7533: Part 3: 1997. London: British Standards Institution.

11 **TRL Limited (2003)**. *Footway and cycle route design, construction and maintenance guide.* Application Guide AG26 (Version 2). Crowthorne: TRL Limited.

12 **British Standards Institution (1995)**. *Methods of testing cement. Part 1: Determination of strength.* BS EN196-1:1995. London: British Standards Institution.

13 **British Standards Institution (1995)**. *Methods of testing cement. Part 3: Determination of setting time and soundness.* BS EN196-3:1995. London: British Standards Institution.

14 **British Standards Institution (1995)**. *Methods of testing cement. Part 5: Pozzolanicity test for pozzolanic cements.* BS EN196-5:1995. London: British Standards Institution.

15 **British Standards Institution (1995)**. *Methods of testing cement. Part 2: Chemical analysis of cement.* BS EN196-2:1995. London: British Standards Institution.

16 **United States Environmental Protection Agency**. EPA 1312 Leach Extraction Test. Retrieved: 2004, from http://www.epa.gov/SW-846/pdfs/1312.pdf

17 **Keeling A A and Marchant L (2001)**. *Grass and tree growth in synthetic soils - early results.* Presented as Appendix 4, Brite Euram Project Report BE97-5078 'Refill', Final Technical Report by Tarmac Fleming November 2001.

18 **British Standards Institution (1994)**. *Specification for topsoil.* BS 3882:1994. London: British Standards Institution.

19 **The Council of the European Union**. Council Directive 1999/31/EC of 26 April 1999 on the landfill of waste.

20 **British Standards Institution (1990)**. *Methods of test for - soils for civil engineering purposes. Part 9 In-situ tests.* BS 1377-9:1990. London: British Standards Institution.

21 **Bowles J E (1984)**. *Physical and geotechnical properties of soils.* 2nd edition, pp. 251-252. London: McGraw-Hill.

Appendix A: Applications considered

Particle size (mm)		0.060	0.200	0.600	2.000	
BS 1377 Classification	Fines	Fine sand	Medium sand	Coarse sand	Gravel

Sandstone quarry sand

Sports activity
- Ski slope surface
- Artificial sports pitches, replacement of fine sand in Astro-Turf

Horticulture
- As grit for aeration of peat compost
- Ornamental grits
- Specialised use for planting tropical plants or heather if acidic
- Use in base of pots for weight and as a drainage layer
- Vermiculite replacement for very fine seeds
- Micro-mulch for nursery production of seed-propagating plants
- Bespoke artificial soil – use in land regeneration projects
- Use as fill on golf courses
- Horticultural grit (for forestry applications)
- Soil in sheaths for revegetating arid areas(e.g. dunes)
- Sand based soil for urban tree planting
- To improve low quality soil (rock dust used in Scotland)

Construction
- A PFA substitute
- A cement substitute
- Slurry sealed aggregate for anti-slip walkways
- Coloured mortar sand for restoration of buildings
- For filling of hairline cracks in reinforced concrete
- For cement replacement in grouting
- Bulk fill on embankments
- Cement stabilised road sub base
- Concrete products – blocks, paving slabs, ornamental products
- Drainage medium
- Local special stage rally roads
- Forestry Commission roads / rural cycle paths
- OPC replacement
- Road sub-base
- Substitute for Block Paving Sand
- High friction road surfacing / micro slurries
- Synthetic lightweight aggregate

Environmental
- Acid mine discharge – organic containment
- Beach restoration / coastal defence schemes
- Bulking / dilution in ex-situ bioremediation schemes
- Daily cover on landfill sites
- Accelerated Carbonation plant for production of aggregate
- Soil improvement/bioremediation schemes if large fine fraction
- Soil improvement/bioremediation if large coarse fraction
- Mixed with bentonite as basal liner for landfill sites / reservoirs
- Underneath / above HDPE landfill liners to prevent punctures

Manufacturing
- Alternative to primary fillers
- Brick manufacture
- Insulation material
- Sand bags
- Shot blasting / metal polishing
- Paint manufacture
- Tile manufacture

Key

Required [ ]   Permitted [ ]   Prohibited [ ]

1 Shotblasting using this material would not be allowed as use of sand in this application is now illegal due to risk of silicosis.

2 The use of the material as a high-friction surfacing (as a replacement for calcined bauxite) was trialled at laboratory scale but was found to be unsuitable as it was not sufficiently durable.

Appendix B: Case studies

Incorporation of sandstone quarry sand into structural concrete C20 – C50

Research has identified that approximately 3.8 million tonnes of crushed rock 'fines' are produced annually in South Wales, a significant proportion of which comes from sandstone quarries, and are referred to as Sandstone Quarry Sand (SQS). 25% of the quarried rock comprises SQS (≤ 3.5 mm) for which there are currently limited markets. TRL has undertaken a two year project to investigate new market applications for SQS. One established market for the SQS is use in concrete.

Hanson Aggregates manufacture structural concrete at a plant located within Craig-yr-Hesg quarry (South Wales) using 12% unseparated Sandstone Quarry Sand.

- Crushed concrete cubes from the quarry supplied to TRL had 7-day strengths of 32.0 and 34.0 N mm^{-2}.

- The product is sold as standard C35 strength concrete.

If the SQS material produced at the quarry were to be screened (e.g. removing the sub 75 μm for use in other processes such as those being investigated by TRL), then a far greater proportion of the coarser grained material could be incorporated into the mix.

Block making aggregate

Sandstone Quarry Sand is also known to be used in block manufacture. It requires 10% of 6 mm aggregate to be added to prevent balling and voids. It is understood that a number of block manufacturing companies in South Wales use SQS in their mixes at various rates, and that the blocks achieve 28-day strengths of 7 N/mm^2.

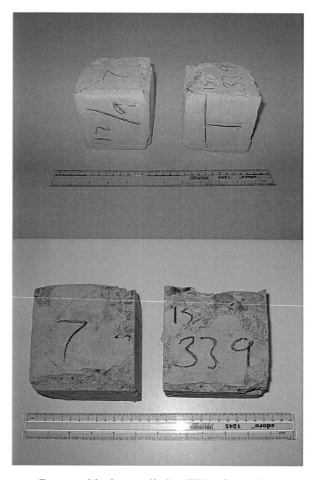

Concrete blocks supplied to TRL after testing

For more information, contact:

Dr. John Lewis
jlewis@trl.co.uk
+44 (0)29 2066 0117

Mr. Martin Lamb
mlamb@trl.co.uk
+44 (0)29 2066 0117

Sandstone quarry sand in cement bound road sub-base

Research has identified that approximately 3.8 million tonnes of crushed rock 'fines' are produced annually in South Wales, a significant proportion of which comes from sandstone quarries, and are referred to as Sandstone Quarry Sand (SQS). 25% of the quarried rock comprises SQS (≤ 3.5 mm) for which there are currently limited markets. TRL has undertaken a two year project to investigate new market applications for SQS.

Physical data has suggested that the material would form a good sub-base in terms of strength and compaction, but it may be susceptible to frost heave in unbound applications. It also fails the requirement for crushed rock unbound sub-base to be non-plastic.

Previous research has been conducted by others into the manufacture of a non-plastic sub-base from siltstone and sandstone dust through the addition of scalpings and various additives to break down the clay minerals present.

However, the most economic option was to blend a 0-1 mm fraction that had been washed out of the 0-2 mm fraction, with the 0-2 mm dust. This diluted the <425 μm and <75 μm fractions, and hence reduced the plasticity. The washing process resulted in a surplus of washed out filler so there still remained a disposal problem, albeit more manageable.

If an appropriate use could be found for the filler, this application has potential for quarries in South Wales. It is possible however, that if material were to be screened, then higher value applications may be sought.

The SQS would, however, comfortably meet the specification for a CBM1 cement bound sub-base, and could therefore be used in a local highway application if economical. The material would be likely to have too great a proportion of fines to be considered for a CBM2 sub-base.

Testing was carried out by Minton, Treharne and Davies to determine the cement content required at 100% compaction to meet the strength requirements of the CBM1 standard. Tests were carried out in accordance with BS1924: Part 2:1990.

Mixes were carried out at 50, 75, 100 and 125 kg/m^3 cement contents based on a density of 2,200 kg/m^3. Test cubes were compacted at a moisture content of 9% by mass of aggregate. Three 150 mm cubes were made at each cement content, cured in accordance with BS1924 and crushed at seven days. The mean results of the testing are presented in the graph above.

The cement blocks displayed a steady increase in compressive strength with cement content, with the 4.5 N/mm^2 requirement for CBM1 falling between cement contents of 75 and 100 kg/m^3. In practice, the higher cement content (100 kg/m^3) would be used to ensure the strength was achieved.

The CBM1 7 day compressive strength requirement of 4.5 N/mm^2, when using 100 kg/m^3, would be achieved by adding approximately 4% of cement to the SQS.

For more information Contact

Dr. John Lewis
jlewis@trl.co.uk
+44 (0)29 2066 0117

Mr. Martin Lamb
mlamb@trl.co.uk
+44 (0)29 2066 0117

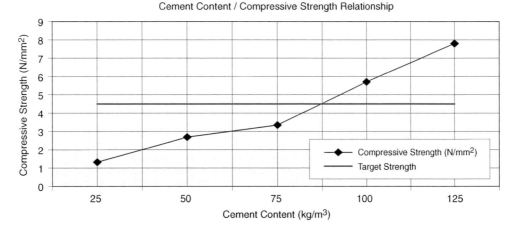

Strength for cement blocks

Case Study

Sandstone quarry sand in cycle paths

Research has identified that approximately 3.8 million tonnes of crushed rock 'fines' are produced annually in South Wales, a significant proportion of which comes from sandstone quarries, and are referred to as Sandstone Quarry Sand (SQS). 25% of the quarried rock comprises SQS ($\leq$ 3.5 mm) for which there are currently limited markets. TRL has undertaken a two year project to investigate new market applications for SQS.

One possible application of SQS is its use in cycle paths. Analysis of the SQS suggests that the material could be used to construct a strong, well-compacted structure with good load bearing characteristics.

Demonstration trials

A TRL demonstration project of SQS in cycle-path applications was undertaken at the Afan Argoed Country Park, near Port Talbot. This was constructed in February 2004 following consultation with Neath Port Talbot County Borough Council (who operate the park) and SUSTRANS. RMC provided the SQS (from their Gilfach quarry) used in the cycle-path. Gerald Davies Ltd provided plant and labour for construction.

For the trial, a 2 metre wide, 60 metre long section of cycle path has been divided into three 20 metre sections respectively comprising, compacted SQS, SQS with Ordinary Portland Cement (OPC) binder and SQS mixed with a coarser material. The section using OPC as a binder has been further sub-divided into four 5 metre long sections with varying cement contents (1.0, 1.5, 2.0 and 2.5 %) to assess which mix performs best. A further section of trial cycle path encompasses a tight bend made of SQS and 4.2% OPC binder. This section is intended to demonstrate the performance of bound SQS in an area anticipated to receive heavy wear due to mountain biking.

The material has been observed to perform well, with the unbound section having the best overall appearance.

Following the success of the site trials, a local BMX track has been resurfaced using SQS.

Following the completion of the site trials, a guide for the use of SQS in cycle paths will be produced to enable the recommendations of the research to be implemented in the South Wales area and elsewhere.

For more information Contact

Dr. John Lewis
jlewis@trl.co.uk
+44 (0)29 2066 0117

Mr. Martin Lamb
mlamb@trl.co.uk
+44 (0)29 2066 0117

Use of sandstone quarry sand in manufactured soils

Research has identified that approximately 3.8 million tonnes of crushed rock 'fines' are produced annually in South Wales, a significant proportion of which comes from sandstone quarries, and are referred to as Sandstone Quarry Sand (SQS). 25% of the quarried rock comprises SQS ($\leq$ 3.5 mm) for which there are currently limited markets. TRL has undertaken a two year project to investigate new market applications for SQS.

One possible use of SQS identified is as the principle component of a manufactured topsoil. The relevant British standard (BS 3882:1994 – Specification for Topsoil) specifies requirements for three grades of topsoil: Premium grade, General-purpose grade and Economy grade. Each soil grading has a corresponding list of criteria that must be satisfied. These criteria pertain to the following soil properties:

- Textural classification.

- Maximum stone content.

- pH value.

- Nutrient content (N, P, K, Mg).

- Loss on ignition (LOI).

- Exchangeable sodium percentage.

- Source location to within 100 m (Premium grade requirement only).

Past and current research into artificial soils suggests blending mineral surpluses such as SQS with organic materials (e.g. composted green waste or agricultural waste) might produce a suitable artificial soil. Initial work has shown that by using a 70:30 v/v blend of either the filler fraction (< 75 μm) or unseparated SQS and a suitable organic material, the textural classification and stone size requirements of Premium grade topsoil can be achieved. The filler fraction typically meets the grading standards required for Premium topsoil, whereas the unseparated SQS does not. To achieve premium grading, it is required that the source of the topsoil be specified to within 100m. It is questionable whether this could be done with a manufactured soil, although the source of the separate soil components could be specified (i.e. the particular quarry that supplied the SQS and the location of the compost supplier).

The filler fraction comfortably meets the Premium grade topsoil textural specification. However, in addition to the physical and textural requirements for

General-purpose grade topsoil, there are a number of chemical and nutrient requirements that must also be met. It is anticipated that by mixing ~ 30 % compost with the SQS that these chemical and nutrient requirements will be fulfilled.

Trials

Trials of the performance of grass growth on various blends of SQS (separated and unseparated) and organic matter were undertaken at the Geoenvironmental Research Park (GRP) in South Wales.

Each of the six test beds (divided into four sub-sections) measures 3m by 3m. The test bed substrates comprise various combinations of SQS (unseparated and filler fraction), compost, local topsoil, manufactured topsoil and fertiliser, as shown in the diagram above.

The test beds were seeded with a standard DoT Pro 85 grass seed mix (used for highway embankments) and the performance of subsequent grass growth monitored using a modified Braun-Blanquet scale over the growing season (April – September) so that grass performance on the various substrates can be collated and compared.

It was found that both SQS and filler mixed with topsoil can sustain excellent vegetation growth, as shown in the picture above, and can form an ideal topsoil replacement.

For more information, contact:

Dr. John Lewis
jlewis@trl.co.uk
+44 (0)29 2066 0117

Mr. Martin Lamb
mlamb@trl.co.uk
+44 (0)29 2066 0117

Case Study

Use of sandstone quarry sand as a cement extender

Research has identified that approximately 3.8 million tonnes of crushed rock 'fines' are produced annually in South Wales, a significant proportion of which comes from sandstone quarries, and are referred to as Sandstone Quarry Sand (SQS). 25% of the quarried rock comprises SQS ($\leq$ 3.5 mm) for which there are currently limited markets. TRL has undertaken a two year project to investigate new market applications for SQS.

Market research indicated that there was a potential to use SQS as a component of a cement substitute using a process developed by fellow GRP project partner E&IE. Subsequently laboratory trials were performed by E&IE on this substitute cement. The investigation of the chemical and physical properties was determined over a period of six months using the methods listed as follow:

- Mortar prisms were produced and tested over a period of 90 days in accordance with BS: EN 196 part 1:1995 for determination of strength.

- Chemical analysis (whole sample): dried and crushed samples were prepared (lithium metaborate method), acid digested and analysed using ICP-OES. Analysis included both major and trace elements which were compared against E&IE's materials database. Coupled with physical analysis this gave an early indication of the performance of the material.

- Soundness: test samples were prepared and tested for soundness over 24 hours using Le Chatelier apparatus, carried out in accordance with BS EN 196 part 3: 1994 for determination of setting time and soundness.

- Pozzolanicity: testing was undertaken in accordance with BS EN 196 part 5:1994.

- The determination of free lime, loss on ignition, insoluble residue and sulphate was carried out in accordance with BS EN 196 part 2:1994. The Na_2O equivalent was calculated using the method set out within the standard.

- Leach testing: The EPA 1312 Leach Extraction Test was adopted. The test was carried out using a liquid / solid ratio of 2:1 (100ml of water to 50g of material sample); the mortar sample was dried and milled to 100 % passing 4 mm.

Summary

Chemical and physical analyses of the mortar indicated that SQS could be used as a component of cement substitute or a concrete extender. Its use in this application will be subject to the requirements of the end user and the availability of other materials that are required to make the cement substitute.

Leach test results did, however, indicate a significant increase in the leaching of lime from mortar samples with the SQS addition. This is potentially problematic because this could result in efflorescence on concrete products made from this material. Potassium and sodium concentrations in the leach tests were found to be much lower than for that of Ordinary Portland Cement. Although giving a positive result for pozzolanicity, the very high insoluble content of the material means that the SQS would act purely as a filler limiting the quantity used in a cement substitute.

At present, operational issues at local quarries in South Wales would limit the use of SQS in this application. Further research could be undertaken in the future if operational conditions become more favourable.

For more information Contact

Dr. John Lewis
jlewis@trl.co.uk
+44 (0)29 2066 0117

Mr. Martin Lamb
mlamb@trl.co.uk
+44 (0)29 2066 0117

Case Study

Sandstone quarry sand as block paving bedding sand

Research has identified that approximately 3.8 million tonnes of crushed rock 'fines' are produced annually in South Wales, a significant proportion of which comes from sandstone quarries, and are referred to as Sandstone Quarry Sand (SQS). 25% of the quarried rock comprises SQS (≤ 3.5 mm) for which there are currently limited markets. TRL has undertaken a two year project to investigate new market applications for SQS.

SQS has been used locally as block paving bedding sand, although the material does not meet the grading specifications given in BS 7533. However, if the material is screened to remove the 75 μm fraction, the material falls within the required grading envelope.

In order to assess the performance of SQS as block paving bedding sand, three block paved parking bays were constructed using standard control bedding sand, SQS with the <75 μm fraction removed and unseparated SQS.

Gerald Davies Ltd were contracted to undertake the trial at their premises in Margam, near Port Talbot and Hanson supplied the 4 tonnes of SQS and >75 μm SQS required for the trial.

Construction was carried out in accordance with Application Guide AG26 ('Footway and Cycle Route Design, Construction and Maintenance Guide'). The bays were marked out using concrete kerbing with a crushed rock sub-base over which 30 mm concrete slabs were laid and compacted.

Optical levels were taken at key points on the bays prior to commissioning and regular visual inspections are being carried out.

The parking bays received constant usage throughout the working week and so provided proved useful in assessing the performance in a live environment.

Measurement of the levels after ten months of use indicate that all three bays including the kerbs have settled, although there was no obvious drop in levels or rutting visible except on one corner of Bay 1, the control sand bay. A total of 40 measurements were taken in each bay with the largest average and single downward movement recorded in Bay 1 of 3.13 and 5.00 mm respectively.

Bay 2, containing unseparated SQS had an average downward movement of 2.05 mm with Bay 3, the >75 μm bay performing marginally better with an average downward movement of 1.83 mm.

The results of the monitoring clearly indicate the SQS is a suitable material for use in this application, with both the separated and unseparated material outperforming the control marine sand. As the performance of the unseparated material was so near to that of the washed SQS, it is considered that with adequate moisture control there would be no requirement for additional processing.

For more information, contact:

Dr. John Lewis
jlewis@trl.co.uk
+44 (0)29 2066 0117

Mr. Martin Lamb
mlamb@trl.co.uk
+44 (0)29 2066 0117